My Lucky Dreidel

Hanukkah Stories, Songs, Poems, Crafts, Recipes, and Fun for Kids

Cherie Karo Schwartz

Illustrations by Wendy Edelson
Photography by Jonathan Gross

SMITHMARK

A MAGNOLIA EDITIONS BOOK

© 1994 by Magnolia Editions Limited
Text © 1994 Cherie Karo Schwartz
Photographs © 1994 Jonathan Gross
Illustrations © 1994 Wendy Edelson

This edition published in 1994 by
SMITHMARK Publishers Inc.
16 East 32nd Street, New York NY 10016.

SMITHMARK Books are available for bulk purchase for sales
promotion and premium use. For details write or call the
manager of special sales, SMITHMARK Publishers Inc., 16 East
32nd Street, New York, NY 10016; (212) 532-6600.

ISBN 0-8317-6285-3

Library of Congress Number 94-066788

My Lucky Dreidel
Hanukkah Stories, Songs, Poems, Recipes, Crafts, and
Fun for Kids
was prepared and produced by
Magnolia Editions Limited
15 West 26th Street
New York, NY 10010

Editor: Karla Olson
Art Director: Jeff Batzli
Layout: Jennifer S. Markson
Photography Director: Christopher C. Bain
Production Manager: Jeanne E. Kaufman

Color separations by Bright Arts (H.K.) Ltd.
Printed and bound in China by Leefung-Asco Printers Ltd.

10 9 8 7 6 5 4 3 2 1

SOURCES FOR STORIES AND FOLKLORE

CHAPTER 1: LIGHT
STORY: Hanukkah story: Book of the Maccabees, from
accounts by Joseph Flavius and rabbis. Midrash of enemy
spears used to create new menorah: *Pesitka Rabbati:
Discourses for Feasts, Fasts, and Special Sabbaths* (2.1). Finding
of one cruse of oil that lasted eight days: *Megillat Taanit* (9)
and the Babylonian Talmud (Shabbat 21b).

CHAPTER 2: FAMILY
STORY: Story contains common folktale themes: three
children sent on a mission, wishes, giving of money to do
good, helping strangers, giving to the poor, youngest as
wisest. A derivative story, which I came across years ago, is
by Joy F. Moss. I have done extensive research to try to
discover the source of this story, but have not been
successful. Any further sources would be appreciated.

CHAPTER 4: FREEDOM
STORY: There are hundreds of variations on the basic idea of
the gingerbread man, or the runaway food.

CHAPTER 5: REDEDICATION
STORY: The story of the one cruse of oil: *Megillat Taanit* (9)
and the Babylonian Talmud (Shabbat 21b). Various versions
call the finder of the oil a young boy, the son of a priest, or a
woman. In my adaptation of the traditional tale, I chose to call
the finder a "young child."
POEM: Based on the account of the rededication of the
Temple: I Maccabees.

CHAPTER 6: MIRACLE
STORY: Adaptation of an Egyptian folktale found in the Israel
Folktale Archives (IFA); collected by Dov Noy at IFA; told to I.
Zohar by her mother, Flora Cohen, in Egypt (found in English
translation in *70 and 1 Tales for the Jewish Year*, by Barbara
Rush and Eliezer Marcus).

CHAPTER 8: HOPE
STORY: Adaptation of an Eastern European folktale recorded
for IFA, told by David Ha-Cohen. There are many variants in
Jewish folklore on the theme of being saved by a light in the
darkness.
RECIPE: The story of Judith and Holofernes: The Book of
Judith, Apocrypha.

Dedication

To Rabbi Yosef Karo, mystic, interpreter, storyteller, and perhaps my ancestor through my father's family. The angels rested on his shoulders and whispered stories to him. I listen.

Acknowledgments

This book has been a magical journey for me across 2,000 years and almost thirty countries to gather the stories, folklore, recipes, crafts, music, and poetry about Hanukkah. I never could have made the voyage safely without the love and the faith of many people. I wish to especially thank my family, all of them, for believing in me and the stories. *Todah rabbah* Larry, Mom, Dad, Sandy, Donna, Brad, Christopher, and Michael. My mom, Dotty Karo, a sewing magician, is a wonderful co-creator of the crafts and recipes, and a constant supporter. My sweet husband, Larry, helped bring life to the poetry and crafts. He has eyes and ears and heart of gentle strength, and is a great story listener, as are our two fourteen-year-old cats, Shosha and Inkling. My heart-friend Peninnah Schram, the *maggidah* of Jewish storytelling, is here for me with encouragement, wisdom, and patience.

Others helped with the itinerary of the trip and the *takhlis*, or business end of matters. Two great Jewish folklorists and friends, Howard Schwartz and Barbara Rush, helped with sources and technical questions. Anita Wenner and Bernice Tarlie, librarians with knowledge and heart, helped me wade through sources and stories to find just the right answers. Anita Fricklas helped me edit my first version of the story of Hanukkah years ago. Joy F. Moss inspired me with the idea for "The Very Best Hanukkah Gift" and Roanne Spector with the idea for the Peace Mats. To all, my thanks and appreciation.

I would like to acknowledge Dorothy Sachs for all of her help and the United Synagogue of Conservative Judaism for their permission to use the following songs (in Hebrew, transliterated, and in English): "Sov Sov S'vivon," "My Dreydl," and "Mi Y'maleyl" (from *The Songs We Sing*, selected and edited by Harry Coopersmith, copyright 1950 by the United Synagogue of America, used with permission of the publisher, The United Synagogue Commission on Jewish Education).

I also want to thank Caryn Malitzky of Magnolia Editions for her vision of creating this unique book and for her faith in choosing me to write it. And I would like to extend special thanks to Karla Olson for her valuable insights and comments in editing this book and for her clarity in helping to bring my thoughts to light.

And to all the children and adults all over the country who have heard me tell and teach for half my lifetime, who have listened with imagination and soul, and who have shared their own stories, too: my special thanks, and all wishes for long and happy lives filled with good stories.

Included in this book are sources for historical and folklore materials used within. Some are very hard to trace; their sources in other books are given as "legend," "story from the Rabbis," or "Midrash." Wherever possible, I have traced the source to a folktale, midrash, historical, or biblical account. I apologize for any omissions.

Contents

Introduction

Welcome to the whole wonderful world of Hanukkah—filled with celebration, memories, traditions, history, and fun. Like all Jewish holiday celebrations, Hanukkah is unique. Our holidays developed over hundreds or even thousands of years. They were changed by time and also by the different places where the Jews have lived in their search for religious freedom. Hanukkah celebrations are very different for children living in Israel, Russia, and Morocco than they are for children in North America, but they all have certain customs in common. Most important, they all celebrate the victory of the brave Maccabees over an enemy who tried to take away the religious freedoms of the Jews. Each celebration includes a lamp with candles or oil for eight nights, one light for each night of the holiday. There are also prayers, songs, and family involvement.

Ride a magic carpet across time and continents to discover how Hanukkah is celebrated in many Jewish cultures, to rediscover familiar traditions, and to create new ways to enjoy the holiday. You may find some traditions of your family's ancestry or interesting Hanukkah practices that will be fun to incorporate into your own family, synagogue, or school celebrations. Use this book to make your Hanukkah brighter and even more enlightening this year!

This book contains eight sections, one for each of the nights of Hanukkah. Each section highlights one of the themes of the holiday: light, family, challenge, freedom, rededication, miracle, hope, and peace. Each is filled with information, projects, and activities: a story, poems, songs, a recipe, a craft, and folklore from the Jewish communities of the world. You can find out about Hanukkah customs from many countries around the world.

Because the stories and customs come from all over the world, we have tried to use the words for the holiday symbols that would be used in each country. This means that some of the words change from country to country and story to story. For instance, in stories that take place in Eastern Europe (the Ashkenazic tradition), the candle holder is called a *menorah*, but in the Sephardic tradition (Jews of Spain and Portugal and their descendants), it is a *hanukkiya*. In Ashkenazic Hebrew, the candle that is highest and lights the rest of the candles is called the *shammes*, and in Sephardic Hebrew, it is the *shammash*. Today, in many synagogues and schools, the symbols are called by their Israeli names, but in some traditional settings, the Ashkenazic term is still used. In this book, we use the best word for each time and place. We hope you do not get confused.

This book is your passport to the history and the practices of Hanukkah. Enjoy learning about the many different customs, reading the stories, making and eating the foods, creating the crafts, singing the songs, and reciting the poetry. Then, have fun thinking of wonderful new ways to celebrate with your family, friends, and neighbors on Hanukkah!

CHAPTER ONE

Light

Genesis, the first book of the Torah, teaches that in the beginning there was only darkness, and light was the first thing created in the universe. Because of this, light has always been important in Judaism. For example, there is the Ner Tamid (nehr tah-MEED; eternal light), which always shines over the ark in a synagogue; the candles that are lit on Shabbat and other holidays; the candles that are lit in memory of those who have died; and the light that always burned in the Temple at the time of the Maccabees (MAK-ah-beez). There is also the tiny container of oil that was found when the Maccabees finally won their battle, used to light the menorah and rededicate the Temple.

Hanukkah is a holiday that celebrates light. Jewish people all over the world light the candles of the hanukkiya (hah-noo-kee-YAH), the Hanukkah menorah, on each of the eight nights of Hanukkah. The beautiful lights are placed in the window for all to see. On the first night, only one candle (on the right side) of the hanukkiya is lit with the *shammash* (shah-MAHSH). On each of the remaining seven nights, another candle is lit, until finally the whole hanukkiya is lit, filling the room with light. In ancient times, Shammai (SHAH-my), a wise man, thought that on the first night all nine candles should burn, and that each night thereafter should have one candle fewer, showing how many days of the holiday were still to come. Another wise man, Hillel (HIL-el), thought that one should never take away from a blessing or a good thing, but rather add to it. So, he thought, one more candle should be lit each night. The Jews accepted Hillel's thinking, so now each night the hanukkiya glows even more brightly.

Light has been used in many different ways for the celebration of Hanukkah around the world. For the Jews of India, each

Flames So Bright
Larry Schwartz

Sunlight dwindles, hand rekindles
  flames so bright
Burning tapers turn to vapors
  through the night.
With your magic halt the tragic
  loss of light;
Silent clamor calls the Hammer
  and his might.

Hanukkiya is the name that Israelis and other Hebrew speakers use for the candleholder. A hanukkiya has eight branches or other light holders and has one more holder in the middle or on the side, which is set apart from the others.

In this book, we have used the word hanukkiya for modern usage. We have used the words Hanukkah menorah for Eastern European or older American usage.

Blessings for the Lighting of the Candles

בָּרוּךְ אַתָּה יי, אֱלֹהֵינוּ מֶלֶךְ הָעוֹלָם,
אֲשֶׁר קִדְּשָׁנוּ בְּמִצְוֹתָיו,
וְצִוָּנוּ לְהַדְלִיק נֵר שֶׁל חֲנֻכָּה.
בָּרוּךְ אַתָּה יי, אֱלֹהֵינוּ מֶלֶךְ הָעוֹלָם,
שֶׁעָשָׂה נִסִּים לַאֲבוֹתֵינוּ
בַּיָּמִים הָהֵם בַּזְּמַן הַזֶּה.
בָּרוּךְ אַתָּה יי, אֱלֹהֵינוּ מֶלֶךְ הָעוֹלָם,
שֶׁהֶחֱיָנוּ וְקִיְּמָנוּ וְהִגִּיעָנוּ לַזְּמַן הַזֶּה.

Baruch atah Adonai, Eloheynu melech ha-olam, asher kid'shanu b'mitsvotav, v'tsivanu l'hadlik neyr shel Chanukah.

Blessed are you, our God, ruler of the universe, who has sanctified us by Your commandments, and has commanded us to kindle the Hanukkah lights.

Baruch atah Adonai, Eloheynu melech ha-olam, she-asa nisim la-avoteynu bayamim ha-heym baz'man hazeh.

Blessed are you, our God, ruler of the universe, who performed miraculous deeds for our ancestors in days of old, at this season.

(only on the first day)

Baruch atah Adonai, Eloheynu melech ha-olam, shehecheyanu v'kiy'manu v'higi'anu laz'man hazeh.

Blessed are you, our God, ruler of the universe, for giving us life, for sustaining us, and for enabling us to reach this season.

boy and man in the family has his own hanukkiya. All the lamps are hung together on one wall, and when they are all lit, the whole wall is filled with light. In Middle Eastern countries, the hanukkiya was sometimes made out of nine egg shells filled with oil, and the light shone softly through the shells. The Jewish people in Egypt thought that a light in the daytime was more unusual than one in the night, so they lit candles in the synagogue in the morning (without saying the prayers) to remind the people how many candles to light on each of the nights. Then, each night, families lit their hanukkiyot in their own homes. In Yemen, when there was a thriving Jewish community, there was a very special addition of light: Firecrackers were set off in the streets to give bright lights and sound.

There are ways in which you can add more light to your Hanukkah celebration. Develop a family tradition around the way you light the candles, such as parents and children taking turns. Have the youngest light the first candle, then the next youngest, and so on to the oldest. Or light a candle for a member of the family who is no longer alive. You can light each candle in honor of a biblical or other Jewish hero or heroine. Or you can make each candle a symbol of one of the important teachings of Judaism. There are many ways to celebrate Hanukkah, a holiday filled with light!

What is the name for the lamp of Hanukkah? Many people know the lamp as a menorah, a Hebrew word for a lamp of any kind. In recent years, there has been a movement to replace the word menorah with another Hebrew word, hanukkiya, which is a lamp used specifically on Hanukkah.

The menorah is a seven-branched lamp. The first one was made for the tabernacle in the wilderness after the Exodus from Egypt, and it was also used in the First and Second Temples. It held an eternal light. The Temple Menorah was in the Temple at the time of the Maccabees. As far back as the first century, the menorah was the main symbol of Judaism. It is the official symbol of Israel today. There are menorahs in many synagogues.

The Hanukkah lights are sacred, and no work should be done by their light. That is why there is an extra candle, the shammash, which is used to light the other candles. It also stands guard over the rest of the candles.

Light Catcher

On Hanukkah, the hanukkiya is placed in the window, bringing light to the house and the world. A light catcher will brighten your window even more.

MATERIALS:

Two 6, 8, or 10 inch disposable plastic or paper plates (plain or with a decorative border)

1 piece of colored cellophane

pointed scissors or X-Acto knife

hole punch

glitter or sequins

glue stick

string, yarn, or nylon thread

INSTRUCTIONS:

1. Draw shapes on the back of one of the plates. They can be traditional for Hanukkah (dreidels, candles, hanukkiya), or Judaism (star, lion, wine cup), or geometric patterns. You can draw one large shape, shapes in a pattern, or several different shapes. Use only the area inside the rim of the plate.

2. Have an adult help you cut out the shapes with either the scissors or the knife. Start by punching a hole into the plate somewhere along the outline of the shape, and then cut along the outline. Do not cut into the rim.

3. Lay the plate on the piece of cellophane and trace around it. Glue the cellophane over the *back* of the plate with the cutouts. Trim any cellophane that hangs over the edge.

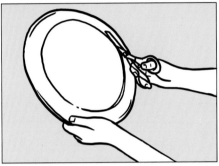

4. Have an adult help you cut out the center of the other plate. To do this, punch a hole along the inner edge of the rim, and then cut along the edge.

5. Glue the cutout rim against the back of the plate with the cellophane.

6. Decorate the front of the plate with glitter and sequins. Spread a small amount of glue wherever you want glitter. Then sprinkle the glitter over the plate. Shake the extra glitter onto a sheet of newspaper so you can use it later.

7. Punch a hole through both of the plates at the top, and attach the string in a loop several inches long, tying it with a double knot.

8. Hang the light catcher in a window.

The Story of Hanukkah

This is a story of how strength and faith, hope and spirit can lead to wondrous victory. It is a story of the Jewish people, and its name is Hanukkah, the Feast of Lights, the holiday of rededication.

Over two thousand years ago, far away in the land of Judea (ju-DEE-ah), now called Israel, the Jews had a beautiful Temple. People came from far and wide to the Temple to pray, bringing baskets of fruit and grain. But the Jews who lived and worshiped there were not completely free. They were ruled by the Seleucids (si-LOO-sids). Unlike the Jews, the Seleucids believed in many different gods. They had a god who controlled the sun, one for rain, one for growing plants, and many others. The Seleucids built statues of their gods and prayed to them. The Jews believed in one God, and they prayed to their God in heaven. Their holidays and celebrations were different from those of the Seleucids, and so were their traditions. However, the good Seleucid king, Antiochus III (an-TIE-oh-kus), let the Jews celebrate their holidays and follow their own traditions.

Eventually, however, Antiochus III died and his son, Antiochus IV, came to power. He did not know much about the Jewish people. The new king's advisors told him that the Jews should believe the same things as everyone else in the kingdom. King Antiochus listened to his advisors and made new laws saying that everyone in his kingdom, including the Jews, would have to observe and worship as he did—worship many gods and pray to the statues. The Jews were told that they would have to change their names, eat different foods, and even wear different clothes. This made the Jewish people very unhappy.

The Jews decided they would not give up their religion and their traditions. The king found out, and he was very angry. How could the Jews disobey him? King Antiochus ordered his soldiers to put Seleucid statues, which were called idols, in the streets. The Jewish people refused to bow down to the idols, so the king told his soldiers to destroy the beautiful religious objects in the Temple, and to bring any gold and silver objects to him. The soldiers did this, and then they put up idols in the Temple. The Jewish people then considered the Temple no longer sacred so they could not worship there. This was in 167 BCE (Before the Common Era).

In the town of Modi'in (moh-dee-EEN), there lived an old man named Mattathias (mat-ah-THIGH-us). He had five sons: John, Simon, Judah, Eleazer, and Jonathan. Mattathias

was the good and wise leader of the town. One day, soldiers of King Antiochus came to Modi'in. They set up a very large idol right in the middle of the town and told Mattathias that he should bow down to the statue god. Mattathias refused. The soldiers became very angry and said that they would do terrible things to the Jews.

Mattathias and his sons called to the Jewish people to follow them into the hills of Judea. They hid in the caves outside of Modi'in where they could be free to worship as they wanted. After Mattathias died, his son Judah became the leader of the small group of Jews. These people wanted to fight to regain their beloved Temple. They had been farmers, shepherds, and teachers, so Judah had to train them to be soldiers. The people began to call Judah the 'Maccabee' (MAK-ah-bee), which means "hammer" because he was such a strong, fierce fighter. The soldiers were called the Maccabees.

The Jews learned fast, and they also used what they already knew. They had been shepherds, so they knew where the caves and safe hiding places were. They hid in the caves and planned their fights, surprising the Seleucid soldiers. In this way, a small group of Jews could defeat a big army of soldiers. They would fight, win, and then disappear back into the secret caves in the hills.

After many victories, the Maccabees had become even more brave and daring. They began to fight out in the open, and they won more and more battles. With each fight, the Maccabees got closer to their Temple in Jerusalem.

In 164 BCE, the Maccabees fought their way toward the city of Jerusalem. When they finally got there, they found idols and statues standing in the streets. They smashed them just as they had smashed their enemies, who had erected the idols. They fought and won more battles in the streets until they came to the Temple.

The Maccabees walked slowly up to the Temple. The Seleucids had made it impure and had let it deteriorate. There were weeds growing in between the steps, and the huge carved wooden doors stood wide open. There were idols standing inside the Temple. The Ark, the place where the sacred Torah scroll was kept, was broken, and the curtains were torn. The Temple menorah was not burning; the Seleucids had taken the golden lamp away and melted it down. It made the Jewish people very sad to see their beautiful Temple in disrepair. They quickly set to work to clean and repair it.

The Jewish people dragged the statues and idols out into the street and smashed them until they turned into dust. They took out the altar, too, because it had been used for worshiping idols. Then they went back into the Temple and cleaned the walls and floors until they shone. They repaired the Ark, fixed the curtain, and put their decorations back.

The Maccabees were able to completely restore the Temple except for one very important thing: they did not have the Temple lamp, for it had been taken by the Seleucids. So the Jews had to make a new lamp, which according to legend, they did by melting down the enemy's spears. The lamp was supposed to burn at all times, day and night, but they had none of the special oil made by the Temple priests. They wanted to rededicate their Temple so that they could worship in it once again, but they needed to light the lamp first. They searched everywhere in and around the Temple for the special oil. Finally, they found a very small jar full, just enough to last for one day. That would be a good start, but it took eight days to make more of the oil. Could they light the lamp and then let it go out again? Should they wait until they could make new oil before lighting the lamp?

The people decided to use the little bit of oil. The lamp was filled, and the flame was lit. Everyone wept with joy to see the light burning once again. Grateful prayers were said.

The people thought they had only enough oil to last for one day. But the next day, the lamp still burned, and the next, and the day after that one, too. It burned and burned with a beautiful flame. That tiny amount of oil kept burning for eight whole days, exactly enough time for the people to make new oil! That was indeed a miracle. But an even greater miracle of the Hanukkah story was that a small group of Jewish people could defeat a huge army, save their Temple, and preserve their right to worship one God as Jews.

In ancient times, sacred olive oil was used for lighting the menorah in the Temple, so olive oil was used in the first hanukkiyot. Later, when candles were developed, they were used in hanukkiyot. In the ghettos and concentration camps of Europe during World War II, crude candles were fashioned out of fat or butter since there were no real ones. Today many people use brightly colored candles that are made in Israel, but some people still use oil lamps. Some people use a hanukkiya with small electric lights for convenience or safety.

Hanukkiya Cake

**Dotty Karo and
Cherie Karo Schwartz**

Hanukkah is a wonderful time of the year for family, friends, and neighbors to get together. It is a perfect time for a party, with lots of food and fun. Of course there will be latkes, and you may want to make some foods with cheese. And you can also create a delicious dessert that will add light to your celebration. Here is a special Hanukkah cake that is very easy to make. It looks just like a hanukkiya, and you can even put candles on top to light it up. If you are careful with them, sparklers can add a bright effect, too! This cake needs to be made of ingredients that are moist, will stay together, and will hold their shape. This one is made with zucchini and wonderful smelling spices, and it tastes great. Surprise your guests with it and see if any of them can guess what is in it!

INGREDIENTS FOR ONE 8 × 12-INCH ZUCCHINI CAKE:

2 cups light brown sugar

3 extra-large eggs (or 5 egg whites), beaten

1 cup vegetable oil

1 teaspoon vanilla extract

1 teaspoon baking soda

1 teaspoon salt

1 teaspoon allspice

¾ teaspoon cinnamon

¾ teaspoon ground cloves

¼ teaspoon baking powder

2 cups grated zucchini

3 cups all-purpose flour

¾ cup chopped walnuts

¼ cup raisins

INGREDIENTS FOR THE FROSTING:

1 cup powdered sugar

2 tablespoons margarine, softened

2 drops vanilla extract or lemon juice

1½ tablespoons milk

food coloring

edible silver or gold cake-decorating balls

TO BAKE THE CAKE:

1. Preheat the oven to 350 degrees F.

2. Mix together the sugar, eggs, oil, vanilla, baking soda, salt, allspice, cinnamon, cloves, and baking powder in a large bowl.

One Little Candle

One little candle shining bright
In our window on this night
Tells the world of spirit and might.
One little candle, a lovely sight.

Two little candles side by side,
Their light can be seen far and wide;
Protected by the shammash guide
They're friends together, dignified.

Three little candles in a row:
Feel their warmth and see their glow.
Their flames wave gently to and fro
Reminding us of long ago.

Four little candles on this day
In their hanukkiya of clay;
Shining so brightly, come what may.
Four little candles show the way.

Five little candles standing tall
In the Hanukkiya on the wall,
Remind us of brave Judah's call.
Five brothers made the enemy fall.

Six little candles' flickering flame
Remember Judah's and Judith's fame,
And Maccabees who overcame
The enemy, who was to blame.

Seven little candles, what a treat:
Candles to watch and latkes to eat.
Celebrate the Maccabees' feat;
They forced the enemy to retreat.

Eight little candles won't last long,
But light they shed is clear and strong.
Recall that right won over wrong.
Come celebrate with story and song.

3. Add the zucchini, flour, walnuts, and raisins, and mix thoroughly.

4. Grease the bottom of an 8 × 12-inch cake pan.

5. Pour the mixture into the pan and bake for 50 to 60 minutes, or until a toothpick inserted into the middle of the pan comes out clean.

6. Remove the cake from the oven and set it aside to cool.

TO CREATE THE HANUKKIYA CAKE:

1. After the cake is cool, place it in the freezer overnight. It will be easier to cut if it is frozen.

2. The next day, take a piece of 8½ × 11-inch plain paper, and draw a large hanukkiya. Be sure not to make the candle part of the pattern too thin. Cut out the pattern.

3. Remove the cake from the pan, and place it on a large dish or cookie sheet. Place the cake on the table, and lay the paper hanukkiya pattern on top of the cake. Secure the pattern with toothpicks.

4. Have an adult help you carefully cut around the pattern with a sharp knife. Then remove the pieces of the cake that are outside the pattern. Set the cake aside.

TO MAKE THE FROSTING AND DECORATE THE CAKE:

1. Mix the powdered sugar, margarine, and vanilla or lemon together. Add just enough milk to make the frosting spreadable. If the frosting is too thin, add a little more powdered sugar. Make two batches of the frosting: One will be white for the hanukkiya, and the other will be colored for the candles. Set one batch aside.

2. Cover the cake with white frosting, but do not cover the section that will be the candles of the hanukkiya.

3. Make your candles colorful. Place small amounts of frosting in several bowls, add a drop of food coloring to each bowl, and mix well. Frost the candles in different colors, then add colored sprinkles to the candles.

4. You can add several little edible silver or gold balls to each of the candles for flames.

5. You can also add brightly colored real candles or sparklers to the tops of your cake candles.

In many countries, the hanukkiya is placed in the front window of the house so that all can see the light and remember the first Hanukkah.

CHAPTER TWO

Family

There are many different kinds of families in Judaism. There is your immediate family—your parents and your brothers and sisters. There is the family of your relatives, including your grandparents and your aunts, uncles, and cousins. The Jews together, from all over the world, are a special family. There is a feeling that the Jews are all one people, no matter where they live in the world. By keeping their faith in the strength of these different types of family, the Jews all over the world have survived for thousands of years.

Hanukkah is a special family holiday. All Jewish holidays are based on history or on biblical events, but Hanukkah is also a celebration of the family. During the holidays, religiously observant Jewish people pray together, eat traditional foods and meals together, and follow special family customs. In this way, the traditions of the holiday are passed from parents to children, and from generation to generation.

There have been times in history when Jewish people were not allowed to gather together to pray, so it became even more important to pass down Jewish beliefs, practices, and rituals through the family, who could still gather together.

During the time of the Maccabees, family again brought strength and power to the Jewish people. Mattathias was a good father and a strong leader. He raised his five sons to respect their religion, their parents, and their freedom. When Mattathias called for the people to fight for the return of the Temple, all five of his sons and many other people followed him. They fought together as a family of Maccabees.

The gathering of family at Hanukkah has always been a beautiful tradition. All over the world, families have celebrated with different customs. In Italy hundreds of years ago, the families rode through Venice in their gondolas (GON-doh-lahs; boats) on one night during Hanukkah, looking for houses with hanukkiyot shining in the window. When they found one, they would stop and sing Hanukkah songs for the people in that

Hanukkah Nights
**Larry Schwartz and
Cherie Karo Schwartz**

Hanukkah nights
we kindle lights

Family all here
Together this year

Sister and brother
Father and mother

Grandparents, too,
say how we grew

Pride in their eyes;
How the year flies

All gather round
hear the prayer's sound

Latkes to eat
our favorite treat!

Driedels to spin
and pennies to win

Candles glow on;
the darkness is gone.

Hanukkah at Our House

(Note: This is my memory of Hanukkah many, many years ago. As you read this poem, you will see that you celebrate Hanukkah in your house in similar ways. What is the same? What's different? It is a great time for families to share their memories and different ways that they can celebrate Hanukkah.)

Hanukkah at our house
is always lots of fun.
With our friends and neighbors,
There are jobs for everyone.

First we will decorate
With ribbons blue and white,
Dreidels, stars, and candles:
Oh what a lovely sight!

Baking is the next step
With rolling out the dough;
Cookies by the hundreds
For everyone we know.

Then the real fun starts
Making latkes: what a treat,
With applesauce as topping;
All of our friends can eat.

Hanukkah at our house:
A time to show we care;
Our family grows closer
On the holidays we share.

home. In Eastern Europe during the last two centuries, fathers of brides-to-be gave their future sons-in-law special gifts on Hanukkah to welcome them into the family. As you read through this chapter, you will learn of customs from other countries that you can make part of your own family celebration.

Today there are many customs and traditions that are great fun for the entire family, as well as for the "extended" family of friends and neighbors. You can play games or make things together, or have a wonderful party for your whole family. If you have a vacation during Hanukkah, you and your family can go on adventures together. You can take some time this Hanukkah to sit down and tell each other stories. But most of all, you can enjoy being a family.

In Eastern Europe in past generations, the children and mother gathered around the father of the house while he lit the Hanukkah menorah and recited the prayers. He then gave each child a coin. After that, the children went to the houses of their other relatives to wish them Hanukkah greetings (and maybe get more coins!). Some of the money went to charity.

In Aden, Yemen, the hanukkiyot were for the boys of the family. Each boy had his own hanukkiya that he would light with all the other males. The hanukkiyot would be placed on the wall. When the boy grew up and got married, he took his own hanukkiya with him to his new house to start a new collection as his family grew. Many of the Yemenite traditions are still carried on with the Yemenite Jews in Israel.

The women of the families of Moroccan Jews tell stories each night during Hanukkah.

In the United States, families celebrate the lighting of the candles with many different customs. In some houses, the children light the hanukkiya, and everyone says or sings the prayers together.

In Syria long ago, the Jews did not use the shammash candle to light the hanukkiya. The shammash (caretaker) of the synagogue gave each family a decorated candle to use to light the candles, and he was paid in appreciation.

Mom's Special Hanukkah Cookies

Dotty Karo

My mom has been making these cookies for almost fifty years. Everyone in our family helps make them. Your family and friends can join in, too. Just get all the ingredients together, put aprons on everyone, and get to work. Some people can press the shapes, some can put the cookies on the sheets, and some can add the colored sprinkles. The dough can get messy, but it is great fun to watch Hanukkah magic come from the cutters. Use cookie cutters in the shapes of dreidels, candles, lions, and Jewish stars, or use a knife to create your own Hanukkah shapes.

INGREDIENTS FOR 3 DOZEN COOKIES:

½ cup margarine

1 cup sugar

1 extra-large egg (or two egg whites)

¼ cup milk

¼ teaspoon vanilla extract

2 teaspoons baking powder

2 cups all-purpose flour

blue food coloring

extra flour for dusting

colored sprinkles

TO MAKE THE COOKIES:

1. Cream together the margarine and sugar.

2. Beat the egg with the milk in a measuring cup. Add the vanilla and baking powder. Mix well.

3. Gradually add the milk mixture and the flour to the margarine and sugar, and mix well.

4. Divide the dough into two equal parts in separate bowls. Make the dough in one bowl blue with about eight drops of food coloring and leave the dough in the other bowl white.

5. Put the dough into plastic bags and refrigerate it overnight, or put it into the freezer for at least 2 hours.

6. When you are ready to make the cookies, preheat the oven to 375 degrees F.

7. Spread wax paper out on a table. Dust the wax paper and a rolling pin very well with flour.

8. Roll out half of each dough at a time to a thickness of ¼ inch.

9. Dust the cookie cutters with flour each time you use them. Press them into the dough one at a time.

10. Carefully remove the cookies from the cutters and place them on an ungreased cookie sheet, about 1 inch apart.

11. Press colored sprinkles on top of each cookie.

12. Bake the cookies in the oven for 8 to 10 minutes, or until they are light brown at the edges.

The Very Best Hanukkah Gift

In a certain town not long ago, there lived a man, his wife, and their three children, Sarah, Jacob, and little Miriam. They were a loving family. They had nearly everything that they could need or want, and they lived a happy life.

One year, just before Hanukkah, the parents called their children together and gave each of them some money. "We have a wonderful surprise for you," their mother said. "Your grandmother, Bubie Rae, is coming for a visit! Bubie Rae always sends you such wonderful presents for Hanukkah, so this year your father and I thought that you might like to each buy her a gift."

The children were very excited. They loved it when Bubie Rae visited, and they were pleased to have a chance to buy her a wonderful surprise. But what should it be? Each of the children went to find a place to think about it.

The oldest, Sarah, went into the garden, and she thought and thought and thought some more. She saw the deep green branches of a pine tree and thought, what a shame. Bubie Rae loves the garden and the flowers so much, but the pine tree is the only one that stays green through the winter. "That's it!" she exclaimed. "I can get my Bubie Rae flowers!" But where could she get flowers in the middle of the winter? Then Sarah remembered something she had seen in a little shop in town that had gifts from all over the world. It was a small stone sculpture from China that looked just like a real miniature tree. It had tiny green stone leaves and bright yellow stone flowers on its branches. It would be perfect! Bubie Rae would have flowers all year long. So off went Sarah to the shop to buy her special present.

Jacob, the middle child, went for a long walk in the woods, his favorite place to figure things out. He listened to the chirping birds, the noises of the small animals, and the sound of the wind rustling through the trees. He walked farther and farther into the woods, where the trees were so thick that they blocked out the sun. Jacob thought about what would be the best present for Bubie Rae. He thought and thought and thought some more. All of a sudden, a cold wind blew through the woods, and Jacob wished that he had his warm coat to wrap around him. "That's it!" he exclaimed. "I'll buy Bubie Rae a nice soft shawl to keep her warm in the winter." So off Jacob went to buy a beautiful shawl the same brown color as Bubie Rae's kind eyes.

Miriam, the youngest child, didn't really have a special place to go and think. She wandered in the garden first, then saw Sarah. Then she wandered into the woods, but no ideas came to her. She wandered along the side of the house where the roses grew in the

summer. She thought about her Bubie Rae, about how good she always smelled, her sweet smile, and the sound of her laughter, how she loved to cook and bake, and how she loved to share a secret with a certain wink. What present would be special enough for her? Miriam thought and thought and thought some more. Then she looked up and saw a bird's nest that looked like a basket sitting in a tree. "That's it!" she exclaimed. "A basket of wonderful Hanukkah goodies will make Bubie Rae very happy!" And off she went to town to fill a basket with Hanukkah gifts.

While the other two children, Sarah and Jacob, were each buying their presents, little Miriam was rushing from store to store, finding just the right gifts for Bubie Rae. She bought a basket big enough to carry many wonderful things. She bought a dreidel and nuts to play the dreidel game. She bought delicious chocolate Hanukkah gelt (coins), and potatoes and onions for making latkes. And she bought a hanukkiya and candles of all colors. She put all of her presents into the basket and started home.

As she was walking, she came upon several children playing outside a small house. As Miriam walked up, the children were asking their friend why his family celebrated Hanukkah and what they did. "Oh, we light candles and get presents," was all that he said. Little Miriam stopped and told them the story of the Maccabees and their bravery, and then took the dreidel out of the basket. She showed them the Hebrew letters on the sides of the dreidel: נ(nun), ג(gimel), ה(hey), ש(shin). "They stand for 'nes gadol hayah sham': a great miracle happened there." She left the dreidel with the children. "Happy Hanukkah," she called as she continued her walk home.

A little farther down the road, Miriam met a poor mother and her three children. They all looked tired and hungry. Miriam thought about her own family, who had everything they needed. But what about this family? Then Miriam had an idea. She gave the food from her basket to the mother, who thanked her again and again. The children looked so happy. "Happy Hanukkah," Miriam called, and then she went on her way toward home.

Just before she got home, Miriam met a blind man walking down the road with a cane. He greeted Miriam as they passed, and she stopped to talk with him. "I remember something about Hanukkah from long, long ago," he said, "but what can a blind man do to celebrate?" Miriam had an idea. She reached into her basket and pulled out the last two things: the hanukkiya and the candles. "Here, take these. Feel the beautiful shape of the hanukkiya and where the candles fit in. When they are lit, you will feel their warmth. Happy Hanukkah!" she called, and she went on her way.

When Miriam got home, her brother and sister were already there with her parents and Bubie Rae. They lit the candles in the hanukkiya for the first night of Hanukkah: one candle and one shammash to watch over it. They said the blessings, and then they all sang Hanukkah songs. After dinner, their parents told Bubie Rae that each of the children had a special surprise for her.

Then Miriam looked at her sister and brother with wide eyes. In the fun of celebrating the first night of Hanukkah, she had completely forgotten the gifts for Bubie Rae and that, without even realizing it, she had given everything away on her way home. All she had left was the basket. What could she do?

Sarah was the first to offer her present to Bubie Rae: flowers in the middle of the winter. Bubie Rae held the beautiful little stone tree with the green leaves and the bright yellow flowers close. "I will treasure this gift always," said Bubie Rae, "because it will remind me that somehow things keep blooming." Sarah smiled. Miriam saw the beautiful little stone tree and she thought, what kind of present will an empty basket be?

Jacob brought out the beautiful, warm shawl the same soft color of Bubie Rae's kind brown eyes, and he told her about the wind in the woods. "I will cherish this gift always," said Bubie Rae, as she wrapped the shawl around her shoulders. "It will remind me that there is beauty that surrounds us and keeps us warm even when times are a little cold." Jacob smiled. Miriam thought, what will I do? I gave away my gift.

"And what did you buy for Bubie Rae, Miriam?" asked her mother and father. Miriam had no choice, so she told about the children and the family and the blind man. Looking down, she handed the empty basket to Bubie Rae. Sarah and Jacob were laughing, but Bubie Rae held the basket close and then put it down. Oh, no, thought poor little Miriam, who was starting to cry. She doesn't like my present at all.

But Bubie Rae pulled Miriam to her lap. "This is a very, very special present, and I will always, always remember it," said Bubie Rae. "You remembered your family, but you shared your present with other families, too. This basket is not empty. It is overflowing with giving and love and promise for the future of the family of all of us. It is a precious gift." And Miriam smiled.

"My wonderful grandchildren," said Bubie Rae, "I love all of you. Each of your presents has brought me special joy. There is joy for my eyes in the sparkle of the stone flowers, Sarah. There is joy for my body with the warmth of the shawl, Jacob. But there is a special joy for my soul for the spirit of family sharing in the basket, Miriam. These are the very best Hanukkah gifts."

Hanukkah Bookmarks and "Family Stories" Book

The Jewish people are known as "the people of the book," and so books and bookmarks are great Hanukkah craft ideas. These bookmarks are simple to make and will show that you put love into creating a present for someone special. You may want to give them to your family along with a book with blank pages that you have decorated. Write a story about your family in the beginning of the book, and then let everyone in the family add stories about the holidays and your family. Older family members can add memories of the generations before yours. This is a present that keeps on giving and growing!

BOOKMARKS

MATERIALS:

1 2 × 2-inch square of colored felt for each bookmark

notebook paper or scrap paper to create pattern

straight pins

needle and thread

polyfill or cotton batting

1 6-inch piece of narrow ribbon for each bookmark

paper clip

sequins

scissors

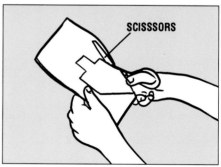

INSTRUCTIONS:

1. Decide what shape bookmark you want to make. You can choose one of the shapes shown or create your own design.

2. Draw the design pattern on the paper and cut it out. Pin the pattern to the colored felt, then cut around the pattern. Repeat so that you have 2 designs of felt, one for the front and one for the back.

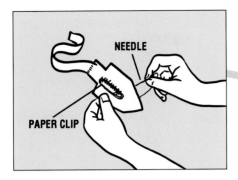

3. Sew 6-inch ribbon to the top of the front piece. Sew sequins around the top side of the bookmark. Sew the paper clip to the middle of the back of the back piece with an overcast stitch. The paper clip should be facing down, so that the bookmark can be placed over the top of a book.

4. Sew the two pieces together, leaving a space to stuff the bookmark.

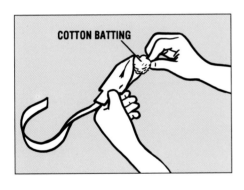

5. Stuff the bookmark with polyfill or cotton batting, and then sew the opening shut.

6. To use the bookmark, clip it to the front cover of a book, and use the ribbon to keep your place as you read.

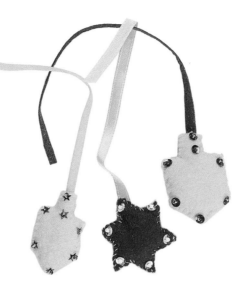

"FAMILY STORIES" BOOK

MATERIALS:

loose-leaf ring binder notebook

lined and unlined notebook paper

sharp scissors

glue

foil letters and stars

family photos

colored felt, fabric, ribbons, lace

INSTRUCTIONS:

1. Fill the notebook with notebook paper. This will be your family stories book. You can add pages or rearrange the pages as your book grows with more stories.

2. Decorate the front cover of the book with memories of your family. You can place decorations right over the front, or you can cover the front and back of the notebook with fabric or felt first. Draw or paint designs or objects your family enjoys, make a collage of pictures, write favorite sayings, or add photographs of your family and their names.

3. On the first page of the book, glue in a photograph or a picture of your family, list family members' names, or draw a family tree.

4. Write an introduction for your book. You can say that this book is for everyone to record their memories so that you all can have a lasting record of your family.

5. You may want to write the first story in the book. It can be your memories of Hanukkah, another holiday, or a family gathering.

6. Ask the whole family to write or draw or paint their favorite memories. Some good categories for stories are: holidays, births, marriages, favorite relatives, earliest memories, how your family got to the United States and to the state where you live, famous people in your family, accidents, funny times, vacations, and food stories. You can add to the book for years to come.

Challenge

Hanukkah is a holiday filled with challenges. In ancient times, the Jewish people faced a great challenge—to win back their religious freedom. A small group of Jews faced a whole army. They hid in caves waiting for the battles. Once they had won the battles and returned to their Temple, they had to clean and purify the Temple for rededication. The Jewish people rose to each of these challenges, and they succeeded.

Throughout history, the Jews have always faced challenges. From the beginning, there has been the challenge of being different, and this has continued wherever Jews have lived throughout the world. Jewish people have faced the challenge of living in many different countries, and of learning to integrate the customs of that country and their own Jewish religion. There has been the challenge of survival, of learning and teaching, and of keeping their faith.

All over the world and throughout time, the many challenges of Judaism have been remembered with different games. In many parts of the world, Hanukkah was the time of the year when people were encouraged to play games, and they were even played in religious schools. In some countries, children performed plays and played games about the victory of the Maccabees. In Eastern Europe, card games were played with decks of cards with Jewish heroes as the "face cards." Dreidels (DRAY-duhls) were made by families each year out of wood or lead and given as gifts. The dreidel has Hebrew letters that remind us of the miracle of Hanukkah. Children also received small coins called *gelt,* which were used for the dreidel game, which was also played with nuts or markers. In the Middle East, in the morning after lighting the hanukkiya at the synagogue, there were picnics with lots of games.

Dreidel is the most popular game of Hanukkah. Besides being just fun, the dreidel may have helped some Jewish people stay alive! During the time of the Romans, Jews were not allowed to

"My Dreydl"
words by Samuel Grossman

I have a little dreydl
I made it out of clay;
And when it's dry and ready
Then dreydl I shall play.

O dreydl, dreydl, dreydl,
I made it out of clay;
O dreydl, dreydl, dreydl,
Now dreydl I shall play.

It has a lovely body,
With leg so short and thin;
And when it is all tired,
It drops and then I win.

My dreydl is always playful,
It loves to dance and spin.
A happy game of dreydl,
Come play, now let's begin.

Hanukkah Riddles

1. The group that was in hiding
Winning battles, law abiding,
Had the name of hammer, and
Can you name the famous band?

2. I am the leader bold
of Maccabees of old,
The father of great fame.
Do you know my name?

3. I am the leader's son.
When he died, I was number one.
They called me the Maccabee.
Now guess: who could I be?

4. The war was fought for years;
There were hard times and tears.
We wanted to return to pray
In this building every day.

5. After the enemy's flight
The Temple needed light.
They didn't use candles, you see;
They found one little jar of me.

6. Today we remember the past.
Eight days celebrations last;
Latkes, gelt and dreidels
Hanukkiya, family and riddles!

ANSWERS: 1. Maccabees 2. Mattathias 3. Judah 4. Temple 5. Oil 6. Hanukkah.

study together, for the Romans wanted everyone to think as the Romans did. If the Roman soldiers saw Jews studying together, they arrested them and severely punished them. There is a legend that the Jews carried tops with them. If they saw the soldiers coming, they took out the tops and pretended they were playing a spinning game instead of studying. So a game saved the Jewish people! Some people say that the tops were the first dreidels. Maybe our dreidel games on Hanukkah are reminders of this ancient challenge.

There are other challenging games you can play on Hanukkah, too. You can have contests to see whose dreidel can spin the longest. You can ask each other lots of challenging riddles. You can play "I Spy" to see who can see the first and the last of the Hanukkah candles turn from flame to smoke. You can play a challenging game of marbles using nuts instead (the nuts aren't round, so they roll all over!). This Hanukkah, why not add more challenges to your celebration? Ask friends and family to bring riddles, puzzles, and other challenging activities to share at your Hanukkah party. It will be that much more fun!

In Modi'in, the village in Israel where the story of Hanukkah took place, a huge bonfire is ignited in the hills. A torch lit from that bonfire is carried by relay teams running from Modi'in all the way to Jerusalem. Important government and religious officials use a flame from the Modi'in torch to light hanukkiyot at the Kotel ha-ma'aravi (the Western Wall) and in other parts of Jerusalem.

In Eastern Europe in the 1800s and the early 1900s, children were asked riddles on Hanukkah. Students were asked challenging questions about their studies, and sometimes the answers were about Hanukkah traditions. Students played card games, and dreidel was the favorite game of the holiday.

In Israel, the sports games of the Maccabiah (mah-kah-bee-YAH; the Israeli Olympics) take place during Hanukkah, and the whole country joins in the celebration. The contestants come from communities of Jews from all over the world to participate in many different sports events. There are games and concerts throughout the country during Hanukkah.

Hanukkiyot Good Enough to Eat

**Dotty Karo and
Cherie Karo Schwartz**

A friend who lived on a kibbutz in Israel said that there was a great contest every year to see who could come up with the most original edible hanukkiya; they were made out of fruits, gefilte fish, and other interesting foods.

A hanukkiya-making contest can be a fun game for any Hanukkah party! Gather many kinds of fruits, vegetables, and sweets. Set up teams, and watch the action. Afterward, everyone will enjoy eating the creations.

Ideas for Ingredients for Edible Hanukkiyot

BASE: canteloupe, honeydew melon, watermelon, zucchini, banana, celery stick, pineapple rings, Lifesaver candies

CANDLES: celery sticks, carrot sticks, asparagus spears, jicama sticks, pretzels, licorice sticks, bread sticks

FLAMES: cherries, raisins, pimientos, grapes, marshmallows, mandarin oranges, olives, cheese cubes, strawberries, pieces of canteloupe

GLUE (to hold ingredients together): cream cheese, peanut butter, hummus, thick frosting

Some Ways to Make a Hanukkiya You Can Eat:

1. Cut a canteloupe in half and cut away the rind. Turn it upside down to form the base of the hanukkiya. Make nine holes around the top of the fruit, and insert apple sticks for candles. Place a red grape on top of each stick as a flame.

2. Peel a firm large banana and lay it on its side. Press in pretzel stick candles and golden raisins for the flames.

3. Cut pear spears for the candles and place them in pineapple ring bases. Place a cherry on top of each for the flames.

4. Lifesaver candies can be the base for licorice stick candles and miniature marshmallow flames.

5. Cut a long piece of celery. Fill the inside of the celery with cream cheese. Cut thin carrot sticks for the nine candles. Insert the carrot sticks into the cream cheese. Add currants for the flames.

The Great Dreidel Challenge

Shira was so happy. She had been searching in all of the shops, and she had finally found the very best, the very finest, the most lucky dreidel! It had to be the one, the only one, that could spin longer than all the other dreidels in the Great Dreidel Spinning Contest. Shira was sure that she had the winning dreidel.

The spinning contest was a traditional school event that everyone looked forward to. A big poster hung at the front of the school with the names of each year's winners and the dreidel's spinning time. A boy named Zak had set the record six years before with a bright red plastic dreidel. Zak came over from the high school a few times to see if anyone beat his record, and he always left smiling. This year, Shira was determined to break it.

Some people showed off their dreidels, but Shira kept hers at home in her top drawer, where her baby brother Aaron couldn't get to it. She only showed it to her best friend, Lucy, who promised that she wouldn't tell anybody what it looked like. The dreidel was dark blue with golden sparkles. Shira knew the Blue Beauty was the longest spinner in the world!

The Great Dreidel Spinning Contest was the talk of the lunchroom; it was hard to concentrate on anything else. People whispered about the best way to hold the dreidel, whether wood, plastic, or metal worked the best for spinning, which fingers to spin it with, and whether oil on the bottom helped. Everyone had different ideas, and each person thought that his or her ideas were right.

The night before the contest, Shira and Lucy sat in Shira's room talking about the contest and practicing with the beautiful blue dreidel. "Jason thinks that his Ruby Racer Dreidel is going to win for sure," said Lucy. "He even talked to Zak about it!"

"Well, the whole school is in for a big surprise. A girl is going to win this year, and I'm going to break Zak's school record while I'm at it!"

Shira's mom was standing in the doorway. "First you need good food to keep up your energy, so come to the table, Shira. Lucy, your mother said you can stay for dinner, so wash up and come on in, girls." Shira realized that she was really hungry, so she and Lucy raced out of the room, leaving the dreidel on the floor. She and Lucy ate fast, anxious to get back to practicing. However, when they went back into Shira's room, the dreidel was gone!

"Look again," her mother called from the kitchen as she did the dishes. "It couldn't have spun off by itself. I'm sure you'll find it in no time." They searched the whole room and

even managed to straighten it up a little, but there was no sign of the dreidel. Shira was ready to cry dreidel theft! But then she heard her mother saying, "No, No, Aaron. That's Shira's dreidel. Here it is, Shira, your baby brother has it."

Shira bent down and took the dreidel out of her baby brother's hands. Half of the handle was missing. "Oh, no!" she exclaimed, "He ruined it!" The most perfect dreidel in the world, and Aaron ruined it. Now it will never spin again. "Oh, my poor dreidel!"

"Shira, dear," said her mother. "You have other dreidels. What about your pretty yellow one from last year? Don't worry; everything will be just fine."

"It won't be fine. You don't understand. I practiced with this dreidel! We were partners. I was going to break the school record!" sobbed Shira.

"Shira could really make the Blue Beauty spin," said Lucy.

"Come on, now, we've got lots of dreidels. You can use one of them, and I think you are going to do a super job in the contest. Cheer up; it's time to do your homework anyway," said her mother. "What do you have left for tomorrow?"

"I did most of my homework, and I never want to see my brother again," sniffed Shira.

"That's not a very good attitude, young lady," warned her mother. "He's only a baby. And, you don't even know for sure that he broke it."

"Well, who else could have done it? I wish that I had my Blue Beauty back together instead of in pieces," said Shira as she started to cry again.

"This isn't getting us anywhere, Shira. You said you've got homework to do, so I suggest that you get it done. You might also want to think about being more patient with your brother. Lucy, you can stay for a while, but only if you see that Shira gets her work done." With that, her mother left the bedroom and closed the door.

"Boy," said Lucy, "I don't think your mom was too happy. But I guess she has a point. Aaron is only a little guy. Babies do break things. So, what homework do you have left?"

"Oh, it's for our special art class. I have to make something three-dimensional and very original. The only problem is that I don't feel very inspired right now."

"Yeah, I see what you mean. This has really been an awful evening. Maybe you can try to get out of your assignment," offered Lucy. "Tell the teacher that you had a bad case of little brother, so you couldn't do your project. Tell her you have a broken heart, and you wish that dreidels were unbreakable." Shira tried to laugh, but she was too unhappy.

The two girls sat in Shira's room for a while, staring at the ruined dreidel. All of a sudden, Shira smiled. "Lucy, you're a genius and my best friend. It's perfect!"

"What did I do?" asked Lucy. But Shira was already off to get her mother's sewing basket.

Her mother saw Shira come racing into the room, grab some supplies, and then disappear into her bedroom again. Over the next hour, either Shira or Lucy came out for more supplies, and then went back. There were noises, sounds, and also laughter. Well, at least there's laughter, thought her mother. But, I hope that they're getting some work done, too.

Finally, Shira and Lucy came out of the room, and Shira had something hidden behind her. "Mom. I'm really sorry that I was such a pain before. I guess that there are some things more important than a perfect spinning dreidel. But Lucy and I figured out a way to make things better all around, OK?"

"That's very nice, dear, but what about your homework?"

"That's all taken care of, too. Hey, Aaron, come here. We have a present for you."

Aaron came toddling over to where Shira and Lucy stood, looking very curious. He loved presents. Mother was at least as curious as Aaron. Shira bent down, and she handed Aaron something small and soft. It was handmade of baby blue cloth, and it had Hebrew letters sewn onto each of its four sides. It had a handle on top and a pointed bottom. It was a dreidel! Aaron took one look at the cuddly dreidel, hugged it and said, "Mine!"

"That is a wonderful surprise for Aaron, a great art project, and a sweet thing for a sister to do, Shira," said her mother. "I am very proud of you. But this dreidel won't spin for very long. What are you going to do about the Great Dreidel Spinning Contest tomorrow?"

The next day, just after lunch, everyone gathered in the gym for the Great Dreidel Spinning Contest. There, high up on the wall, was the poster with Zak's name and the school record. Lucy came over to where Shira was standing in the corner of the room.

"I know how you must be feeling, Shira," said Lucy as she tried to smile. "Well, there's always next year."

"But Lucy, I tried spinning the dreidel holding on to the little piece of the handle. It really works! So the Blue Beauty and I can still be in the contest. But you know what? Even if I don't win the dreidel contest, I know that I've already won something else. I invented a new kind of dreidel. It's made of cloth, so it's soft and safe for babies, and Aaron loves it! Come on, Lucy, let's see what kind of miracle that Blue Beauty can show us!"

Papier-Mâché Dreidel

In many countries for hundreds of years, children have made and played with dreidels. Today most children buy plastic, wood, or metal dreidels, but you can continue an old tradition by making your own dreidel for play. Here is a dreidel made out of a milk carton. It can really spin! You and your friends can make them and have a dreidel-spinning contest.

MATERIALS:

paper milk carton (pint-size)

masking tape

7 ½-inch new pencil, sharpened

colored tape

flour

water

newspaper, cut into about forty 1 × 3 × 6-inch strips

wide-mouthed cup or jar, slightly larger than the milk carton

different-colored paints

INSTRUCTIONS:

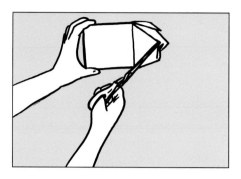

1. Close the spout on the milk carton. Carefully cut along the lines where the carton is folded double at the closed spout.

2. Turn the carton around so that the spout faces away from you. Open this side in the same way that the spout side was opened. Cut the folded sides in the same way that you cut the spout side.

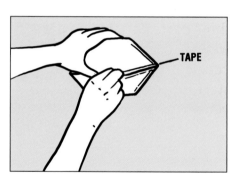

3. Now you have four triangular pieces still attached to the carton, which form a pyramid on top of the milk carton. Tape them together to form the bottom of the dreidel. Set the dreidel aside.

4. Take the sharpened pencil and wrap it with a layer of colored tape. Wrap the tape on a diagonal remembering not to wrap the point of the pencil.

5. Have an adult help you make a hole (slightly smaller than the width of the pencil) in the flat top of the dreidel with a sharp pair of scissors. Carefully insert the point of the pencil in the hole and push it down to the bottom of the dreidel. The points of the dreidel and the pencil will hold the pencil in place inside the dreidel. A few inches of the pencil will be sticking out of the top of the dreidel for the handle.

6. Make a paste by mixing three parts flour to two parts water in a small bowl. Use ¾ cup flour to ½ cup water to start, and make more paste if you need it.

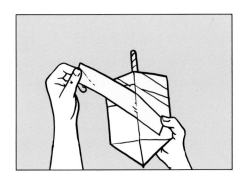

7. Dip newspaper strips one at a time into the flour paste, and place them around the body of the dreidel diagonally. Continue laying on the paste strips until the dreidel is covered with three to five layers of paper.

8. Set your dreidel upside down in the cup, with the flat top on the edges of the cup. Make sure that only a small part of the dreidel is touching the cup, leave the dreidel to dry overnight.

9. When your dreidel is completely dry, paint it. After the paint is dry, paint or draw one Hebrew letter on each side of the dreidel. Make sure the letters are in order—*nun, gimel, hey, shin*—from right to left.

"Sov Sov S'vivon"

**words by S. Bass;
English by Harry Coopersmith
(although his words are not a direct translation, they have the spirit of the original Hebrew meaning)**

סֹב, סֹב, סֹב, סֹב, סֹב סְבִיבוֹן,
מִירוּשָׁלַיִם לְגִבְעוֹן.
מִגִּבְעוֹן סֹב עַד בֵּית אֵל,
וּמִשָּׁם לְיִזְרְעֵאל.
שָׁם קְהַל חֲלוּצִים.
בְּמָחוֹל כֻּלָם יוֹצְאִים.
סֹב, סֹב, סְבִיבוֹן,
רוּצָה, אוּצָה לְגִבְעוֹן.

סֹב, סֹב, סֹב, סֹב, סֹב סְבִיבוֹן,
מִירוּשָׁלַיִם לְגִבְעוֹן.
בַּמַּעְגָּל הִכָּנֵס,
וְלַכֹּל בְּקוֹל הַכְרֵז:
הִנֵּה קָם, הָיָה הַנֵּס,
כָּל הָאָרֶץ-כְּפַרְדֵּס,
מִבְּאֵר שֶׁבַע וְעַד דָּן,
כָּל הָאָרֶץ הָפְכָה גָּן.

Sov sov sov sov sov, sov s'vivon,
Mirushalayim l'Givon
MiGivon sov ad Bet El,
Umisham l'Yizr'el.
Sham k'hal chalutsim
B'machol kulam yotsim.

Sov sov s'vivon
Rutsa utsa l'Givon.

Sov sov sov sov, sov s'vivon,
Mirushalayim l'Givon.
Bama'agal hikaneys,
V'lakol b'kol hachreyz:
Hineh kam, hayah haneys,
Kol ha-arets k'fardeys,
MiB'er Sheva v'ad Dan,
Kol ha-arets hafcha gan.

Spin, my top, around and around
O, spin past bush and pit and
   mound,
Past the vineyard, brook and rill,
Past the valley and the hill,
On to Kishon, my dear.
When you meet a pioneer,
Greet him, bring him cheer;
"Miracles have happened here!"

Unto Modi'in swiftly fly,
And your tidings swiftly cry:
"Maccabeans, rest ye in peace,
Lo, your valiant heirs increase.
Now in place of waging war
They plant vineyards by the score,
Toiling hard, hauling loads,
Building houses, paving roads."

CHAPTER FOUR

Freedom

Do you have many freedoms? Of course you do. You enjoy activities that you choose: to see your friends, to make decisions about where to go or what to do. What if those freedoms were taken away? You would probably fight to get them back, for what could be more precious than freedom? The Israelites fought for their freedom in ancient Egypt over 3,000 years ago, and we remember this fight for freedom today with the holiday of Passover. And Jewish people in many places throughout the world have had to fight for their religious and political freedom in modern times as well. Freedom is precious, and it must be preserved.

Freedom is a major theme of Hanukkah. Over 2,000 years ago, the Maccabees fought for their freedom to worship as they wished. King Antiochus IV decided that if he took away the religious freedom of the Jews, then everyone would believe and behave as he did. But the Jewish people did not give up. They spent the next several years fighting against the whole Seleucid army to regain their religious freedom, and they won. Today we honor their bravery and their commitment to freedom in our celebration of Hanukkah.

Freedom continues to be an important theme of Judaism. There have been many times in history and many places in the world where Jews have been denied their freedoms. They have had to fight to regain them or have had to leave their homes to try to seek freedom elsewhere. Thankfully, though, in the past several years many Jewish people in foreign lands have either been granted their religious freedom or have been allowed to leave for Israel or other parts of the world where they can worship as they please. Israel, the United States, Canada, and many other nations have helped to resettle Jews from Ethiopia, Iran, Iraq, the former Soviet Union, Yemen, and other parts of the world so that they can live freely.

The Jewish people today celebrate their freedom on Hanukkah, just as they celebrate the return to their Temple in 164 BCE.

"MAOZ TSUR" "Rock of Ages" Liturgy

English words by Gustav Gottheil and M. Jastrow

מָעוֹז צוּר יְשׁוּעָתִי,

לְךָ נָאֶה לְשַׁבֵּחַ;

תִּכּוֹן בֵּית תְּפִלָּתִי,

וְשָׁם תּוֹדָה נְזַבֵּחַ.

לְעֵת תָּכִין מַטְבֵּחַ,

מִצָּר הַמְנַבֵּחַ,

אָז אֶגְמוֹר, בְּשִׁיר מִזְמוֹר,

חֲנֻכַּת הַמִּזְבֵּחַ.

Maoz tsur yeshu-ati,
l'cha naeh l'shabeyach;
tikon beyt t'filati,
v'sham todah n'zabeyach.
L'eyt tachin matbeyach,
mitsar ham'nabeyach,
az egmor, b'shir mizmor,
chanukat hamizbeyach.

Rock of Ages let our song
Praise Your saving power:
You amid the raging foes
Were our sheltering tower.
Furious they assailed us,
But Your arm availed us,
And Your word broke their sword
When our own strength failed us.

The Hanukkiya Maccabees

In the hanukkiya candles
My sister says she sees
The lines of freedom soldiers:
They're the brave Maccabees.

She can hardly wait for evening
On each of the eight nights
For the sun to go down again
So we can kindle the lights.

My sister says each candle
Is a soldier fine and brave
Marching on to win battles,
Then hiding in a cave.

She watches all the Maccabees
Standing tall in a row;
She tells me the wonderful story
Of our freedom won long ago.

Mattathias is the shammash
He's the father, number one.
Then come Judah and his brothers;
The great march has begun.

Look into the flames each night
And you can also see
The marching on to freedom
Of the brave Maccabees.

Freedom is also celebrated with foods, like those that the Maccabees ate while they hid in caves during the war for their freedom. For Persian Jews, on the last night of Hanukkah, the father of the house brings a tray of fruits and nuts (like those the Maccabees ate), which the children take to school the next morning to share with friends. In Salonika, Greece, the women make loukoumades (loo-koo-MAH-dehs), believing that it is a food the Maccabees ate. In Syria, kibbeh (KIB-ee) is served. It is a reminder that the Maccabees hid inside caves while they were fighting for their freedom.

In most countries, the people light candles in a hanukkiya. In most countries where Jews live today, they have the freedom to practice their religion and show the world that they are Jewish. During Hanukkah, they place the hanukkiya in a window so that all can see the bright glow and promise of freedom. When you light the candles in your hanukkiya, make a wish for the people everywhere who do not yet have their freedom.

Israel is a land of freedom for Jewish people from all over the world. Even before the establishment of the State of Israel in 1948, Jewish people went to Israel seeking freedom. In the late 1800s and early 1900s, people from Russia who were being persecuted went to live on the harsh land there. Since 1948, Jewish people from many countries where they were not free have escaped to Israel or have been brought into the land by the Israeli government.

The Jewish people of Syria have a very special hanukkiya. It has two shammash candles. Some Jews in the late 1400s found a safe home in Syria after they were expelled from Spain, so the second shammash candle is a reminder of the guarding and protection that led those Jews to freedom in Syria. But after having lived in peace for many years in Syria, the Jews had many freedoms taken away, so they fled Syria and went to other parts of the world, such as Israel and the United States.

In Spain, on the sixth night of Hanukkah, the women make a special sweet couscous dish. Couscous (KOOS-koos) is a Middle Eastern food, so perhaps it is a reminder of the Middle Eastern countries where some of the Jewish people fled to find freedom after they were expelled from Spain in 1492. Perhaps the sweet taste of the food is like the sweet taste of freedom.

Potato Latkes

Dotty Karo and
Cherie Karo Schwartz

Latkes (LAHT-kuhs) are the most traditional of the Hanukkah foods, probably because they are fried in oil, a reminder of the rededication of the Temple menorah. Eaten all over Europe, the Middle East, and in North America, most latkes are made with potatoes, but some, called levivot, are made with flour, and many include vegetables. Some people enjoy latkes plain, while others love sour cream or applesauce with them. No matter how you like them, they are delicious!

INGREDIENTS FOR LATKES FOR 10 TO 15 PEOPLE:

5 pounds potatoes

2 medium-size yellow onions

½ cup matzo meal

1 teaspoon baking powder (optional)

3 extra-large eggs (or 5 egg whites)

salt and pepper to taste

vegetable oil for frying (about ¼ inch at the bottom of the pan)

TO MAKE LATKES:

1. Scrub the potatoes. The latkes are very tasty if you leave the skins on, but you may prefer to remove them.

2. Shred or grate the potatoes, and strain off any juice.

3. Dice the onions, and strain off any juice. Add the onions to the potatoes.

4. Add matzo meal, baking powder, eggs, salt, and pepper and mix well.

5. Have an adult help you heat the oil in a large frying pan or griddle, to medium high.

6. Drop a large spoonful of the latke mix into the pan and flatten it into a pancake with a spatula.

7. Fry the latkes until they are crisp and golden brown, turning them once.

8. Remove the latkes from the pan and place them on paper towels.

9. Serve the latkes immediately with applesauce and/or sour cream.

Variations:

Latkes may be made with apples, zucchini, carrots, or spaghetti squash. Substitute either the grated fruit or grated vegetables for the potatoes, or add equal amounts of fruit and grated vegetable to the potatoes.

The Biggest Latke in the World

Once upon a time, long, long ago and far, far away, there lived a king. He was a mighty king, but also a greedy king. He could have anything he wanted, but once he had it, he always wanted something more.

The king never went out into his kingdom. He just stayed in his big, beautiful castle and relied on his spies to tell him about things in the world. The king claimed all things new and beautiful for himself, threw them into his huge royal closets, then forgot about them.

The king's subjects were very unhappy. Nothing was safe from the king's spies, and the people lived in fear. They were afraid to talk about the good things in their lives. But the people decided that the king was not going to ruin their lives, so they found new ways to live. They traded old clothes, materials, and books, and they told each other stories old and new. They even came to enjoy their lives again. And as long as the king thought that he had the best of everything, there was peace in the land.

That was fine for a while, but then the king noticed that there were no more new things to entertain him, and he got bored. So he called his royal spies and said, "Go out, my servants, all over my kingdom, and find me something that I do not have yet. Do it NOW!"

And so the spies went out across the land. In midwinter, a spy returned from the farthest corner of the kingdom with wonderful news. "Your supreme and g-g-g-greedy, I mean grand majesty," he began, stumbling over his words in his excitement. "I have just returned from the far reaches of your im-impoverished, I mean imperial kingdom, and I have found something that you do not have!"

The cranky king was overjoyed. "What is it? Where is it? Show it to me at once!" he bellowed.

The spy stared at the king, bowed so low that his nose touched the ground, and whispered, "I sincerely regret, Master, that it is something that I heard about, but did not see."

"Then take my entire spy force with you, leave my royal presence, and do not return until you have it—whatever it is! I must have this thing for my very own!"

The spy bowed so low that his forehead touched the ground, then made his way out of the palace accompanied by the spy army. They headed for the farthest corner of the kingdom, traveled over hill, dale, mountain, and valley, and finally came to a little hidden community where the Jews had lived quietly and in freedom for many, many years.

The spies got down from their horses and looked around at the town. Everything looked plain, simple, and peaceful. There were houses, buildings, gardens, and trees. The spies looked around, and then they all complained about coming to the middle of nowhere. The head spy snapped, "Stop whining and just take a sniff!" The spies stopped talking, stopped complaining and, all together, they took one gigantic, greedy sniff. There wasn't a single sound for a second, and then. . . .

"Oh . . . AH . . . UM . . . YUM! It is the most wonderful smell in the world! What is it?"

"I don't know, but it must be what people were talking about when I was here before! They said they couldn't wait for the special something, and I was hoping that maybe one of you would know what it is."

Just then, a smiling old woman came down the road carrying a huge tray of food that smelled . . . DELICIOUS! The spies went rushing toward her. "OH . . . AH . . . UM . . . YUM! Tell us: what do you have there, granny? It has the most delicious smell in the world!"

"Why, these are latkes—potato pancakes!" explained the woman. "They're for Hanukkah, the Feast of Lights. Tonight is the first night of the holiday, and I'm taking these latkes to my sweet grandchildren."

"Oh, no you're not!" shouted all of the king's spies. "The king must have everything new and everything good, and he will have these pancakes!"

"Well, that's all right with me. Here. Tell him that Grandma Millie hopes that he enjoys them in the best of health."

"Tell us," asked the spies as nicely as they could. "How do you make these latkes?"

"Oh, it is the easiest thing in the world," answered Grandma Millie. "All you need are potatoes, onions, eggs, and a little matzoh meal, lots of oil in a big frying pan, and a nice, hot stove. Now, if you'll excuse me, I must go make more latkes for my grandchildren."

"Oh, no, you don't," cried the spies of the king. "The king can have, should have, and will have all of the latkes in the kingdom!"

They followed Grandma Millie to her house and took all of the ingredients for the latkes. Worse than that, they marched all through town—taking all of the potatoes, onions, eggs, matzoh meal, and oil from every house! And then, they got on their horses and rode back to the palace with all speed.

When the spies arrived, the king greeted them. The king was in a royal temper. "Where in the world have you lazy spies been, and where is my newest fine thing?"

The first spy got off of his sweaty, tired horse, touched his chin, nose, and forehead to the ground, and said, "Sire, give us one hour, and we will bring you the biggest, crispiest, most delicious latke in the world."

"Latke? LATKE? What in the world is a latke?"

"Your Royal Greediness . . . I mean Greatness, it is a food that the Jews make for Hanukkah, and I can guarantee that you will love it! Just give us enough time to prepare the first royal latke feast." (What the poor, scared spy had not told the king was that on the long ride back to the castle, the spies had eaten every one of the delicious latkes!)

So, the spies made their way to the kitchens, got down the biggest mixing bowls and the biggest spoons, and began making latke mix. They did not know how much of each ingredient to use, so they used it all. They poured oil onto the griddle and let it get hot. There was so much latke mix that it just barely fit onto the royal griddle! Then the spies sat down to watch the biggest latke in the world sizzling away. The king came in to see what was taking so long. He was so amazed at the wonderful smell that he did something that no one had seen him do for eighteen years: he smiled!

Meanwhile, back in the farthest corner of the kingdom, it had not been a wonderful Hanukkah. True, the people had lit the candles in the windows, said the blessings, told the Hanukkah story, sang songs, and played dreidel. But somehow, it wasn't the same without their favorite Hanukkah food: latkes. Now it was the last night, and no one had tasted potato latkes. ✡

At the palace, the very greedy king couldn't wait for a taste of the delicious-smelling latke. "Give it to me; give it to me NOW!" he bellowed.

"But your Impatient, I mean Imperial One, it is still so light and pale. It needs to be all golden brown," explained the first spy.

The king did not listen. He grabbed the pan and, in doing so, flipped the latke up high into the air. It went sailing right out of the window and down into the valley!

"After that pancake! After it NOW!" bellowed the king to his spies. "It is mine and no one else's! Capture that latke!" All of the poor spies and the king ran out of the palace, climbed on their horses, and went riding off to find the latke that had flown away and was headed for the farthest corner of the kingdom.

In Grandma Millie's house, the whole town had gathered to share their favorite stories about latkes that were plain, apple, jelly, and cinnamon, and served with sour cream and applesauce. Grandma Millie was just telling once again how her latkes had been stolen by the spies when all of a sudden, through the open window flew a huge, still-sizzling, golden-brown latke, the biggest latke in the world! "A miracle! A miracle!" everyone shouted at once. "Our latke found its freedom and came home to us!"

"Everybody grab a fork and enjoy," shouted Grandma Millie. "This latke smells delicious!" They started to eat the latke. Suddenly, they heard the sound of horses and the spies' cry: "Make way for the king!"

All of the townspeople stopped in mid-bite and looked toward the door. It really was the king standing in the doorway, holding a golden fork in one hand. His spies stood behind him, smelling the delicious latke and looking very sad. Grandma Millie took one look at the royal group and said, "Come on in, boys, and join us in our Hanukkah celebration of freedom. Freedom for the Jews! Freedom for the latke!" Everyone laughed, and then they all sat down to a great latke feast. ✡

The king looked around the table at his smiling subjects. How could they all be so happy? Could there be more to happiness than owning everything in the world? "My subjects," began the king, "You have something here that I do not possess, and I want it." All of the people stared at the king. What could they still have? "You have something so great that even I cannot take it away: each other and your traditions. I have only myself and all your possessions. I am lonely! I do hereby decree that you are all invited to the royal palace. Come and see all the beautiful things I have! Take back whatever you need. And . . . please . . . come and visit me sometime. You are all welcome. I have spoken!" And everyone cheered.

From then on, every year in this faraway kingdom of long ago, the people gathered in the farthest corner of the kingdom to celebrate Hanukkah, a holiday of freedom. They celebrated the freedom of the Jews, but they also celebrated the freedom of the king from his greed and his castle, the freedom of all of the people and their possessions, and the freedom of the biggest latke in the world.

The Jewish people in Russia have lived without religious or personal freedoms for hundreds of years. In the last decades, though, many Jews have been allowed to leave Russia for North America, Israel, or other countries. Getting permission to leave can take years and cause even more loss of freedoms. Now there is a large Russian Jewish population in Israel. With more changes in the former Soviet Union, perhaps more Jews will have the freedom to leave.

Hanukkah Go-Round

This is a Hanukkah mobile, where the many beautiful symbols for Hanukkah can all be together and yet be free to move around on their mobile wheel. The mobile brings together many of the symbols of our holiday of freedom.

MATERIALS:

some of last year's Hanukkah greeting cards

colored cardboard

3 yards of gold metallic string

1 8- or 10-inch embroidery hoop, or metal or plastic ring

scissors

hole punch

glitter

glue

3 jingle bells with 18 inches of metallic string

INSTRUCTIONS:

1. Cut pictures and symbols from the Hanukkah cards. Cut a piece of cardboard the same shape for each picture. Glue the cardboard to the pictures.

2. Add glitter to the front and back of the shapes. To add glitter, squeeze glue where you would like the glitter to be. Sprinkle glitter over the shape, then shake the excess off onto a piece of newspaper so you can use it later.

3. Cut the string into nine pieces: two 7 inches long, four 10 inches long, two 12 inches long, and one 24 inches long. Set the 24-inch piece aside.

4. Punch a hole in the top of each shape and thread one of the pieces of string through each hole so that it forms a loop.

5. Tie the shapes, spaced evenly, to the hoop with a knot above and below the hoop. Use different lengths next to each other. Tie one end of the 18-inch metallic string with the bells to each side of the hoop.

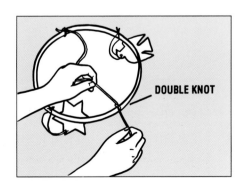

DOUBLE KNOT

6. Attach one end of the 24-inch piece of string to each side of the hoop with a tight double knot. This will be the hanger for the mobile.

CHAPTER FIVE

Rededication

On each of the eight nights of Hanukkah, the lighting of the candles in the hanukkiya is a reminder of the power of light in the darkness. On the first night of Hanukkah there are just two candles, one plus the shammash, and they give off a small amount of light. Each night we add one more candle, and on the eighth night, the whole hanukkiya is lit up with all nine candles. Each night, we rededicate the hanukkiya with light, and each night the light grows brighter. We watch with pride as the candles glow in the hanukkiya in the window. Imagine the pride and joy that the Jews of ancient Israel must have felt when they were finally able to rekindle the lights of the Temple menorah after years of fighting to regain the Holy Temple!

During the reign of the Seleucid king Antiochus IV in the second century BCE, Jews were not allowed to worship in their Temple. The Seleucids made the Temple unclean by taking out all the Jewish objects, putting up statues and idols, and offering sacrifices to their own gods. The Jews—soldiers and families and individuals—dedicated themselves to the task of regaining the Temple, and together they succeeded. After the Maccabees won the war, the first thing that they did was to rededicate the Temple for worship. They cleaned it out, put back the Jewish altar and lamps, and lit the menorah in a beautiful ceremony. The rekindling of the lights was the last step in the rededication of the Temple, so all the Jews could worship together again.

The word *Hanukkah* is a Hebrew word meaning "dedication." The Jewish people remember the rededication of the Temple during Hanukkah, but there are ways to practice rededication all year long. Judaism is dedicated to learning, to good deeds, to helping other people, and to caring for the world. There are times of the year when we take the time to reexamine what we have done, and to think about what we can do to make ourselves and the world a little better. This is called rededication.

Throughout the Jewish world, there are many rededication customs. In Tunisia, the hanukkiya is hung from the doorpost

"Mi Y'maleyl"
Hebrew words by Menashe Ravino; English words by Ben M. Edidin

מִי יְמַלֵּל גְּבוּרוֹת יִשְׂרָאֵל,
אוֹתָן מִי יִמְנֶה?

הֵן בְּכָל דּוֹר יָקוּם הַגִּבּוֹר.
גּוֹאֵל הָעָם.

שְׁמְעוּ בַּיָּמִים הָהֵם בַּזְּמַן הַזֶּה
מַכַּבִּי מוֹשִׁיעַ וּפוֹדֶה.
וּבְיָמֵינוּ כָּל עַם יִשְׂרָאֵל
יִתְאַחֵד יָקוּם לְהִגָּאֵל!

Mi y'maleyl g'vurot Yisrael,
Otan mi yimneh?
Heyn b'chol dor yakum hagibor, go-eyl ha-am.
Sh'ma! Bayamin haheym baz'man hazeh
Makabi moshiah ufodeh.
Uv'yameynu kol am Yisrael
Yitacheyd yakum l'higa-eyl!

Who can retell the things that befell us?
Who can count them?
In ev'ry age a hero or sage came to our aid!
Hark! In days of yore, in Israel's ancient land,
Brave Maccabeus led the faithful band.
But now all Israel must as one arise,
Redeem itself through deed and sacrifice.

Making the Temple Beautiful

After the war was over
And the Temple was regained,
The Temple was in shambles;
The people were deeply pained.

They remembered days of glory
When the great Temple stood
As a light unto the nations
And a symbol of truth and good.

They took out all the statues,
They scrubbed and cleaned and swept.
Grateful prayers were offered;
In gladness, the people wept.

On the twenty-fifth of Kislev,
Three years since they'd been away,
Jews rededicated their Temple
And it was a joyous day.

The curtains hung, the doors set back,
The incense and the wine,
The altar set up at the front;
The Temple looked so fine!

There were cymbals, harps and
   lutes played,
There was music, dance and song.
To honor and rededicate the Temple,
They celebrated eight days long.

Once again the days of glory
And the great Temple stood
As a light unto the nations
And a symbol of truth and good.

opposite the mezuzah (muh-ZOO-zah), a container with prayers, and it is left there until Purim (poo-REEM), the spring feast of Esther, as a reminder of the rededication of the lights. In many countries, adults and children gather food and supplies for the poor on Hanukkah. Jews in some countries rededicate candles from one holiday celebration to another, (a kind of recycling!). In Eastern Europe long ago, the caretaker of the synagogue (called the *Shammes* in Yiddish) collected the drippings from all the memorial candles that were lit in the fall for Yom Kippur. He rededicated them by making candles for Hanukkah. The Jews of Turkey use the bits of wax left over from the Hanukkah candles to make new candles to use in the search for leavened bread on Passover in the spring.

Today we can rededicate ourselves to the world, too. Hanukkah is a good time to think about how to rededicate ourselves to helping others: our families, our friends, the poor and the needy, our community, and the world. What can you do to help? How can you rededicate your life to helping? You can keep your room, your house, your yard, or your neighborhood clean. You can recycle materials, waste less, and help the environment. You can volunteer to help others less fortunate. Think of a good first project, and then take action for rededication!

In Poland in the past, the Hasidic (hah-SID-ik) Jews felt that Hanukkah was a special time to care for the poor. They collected food, clothing, and wood for cooking and heating. They supplied poor households with enough for the whole year. It was also a time to collect money to release Jewish people who were wrongly imprisoned, and to provide help to students studying away from home in the yeshivahs (yeh-SHEE-vahs), the Torah schools.

In the Sephardic schools in Jerusalem, the children go from house to house asking for food for a feast: beans, onions, oil, garlic, and rice. They bring the foods to the synagogue, and, with kettles of food on their heads, they march around the bimah (BEE-mah; platform) seven times. Then the children prepare a feast for the orphans, the widows, and the poor. The feast is called "Miranda de Hanukkah" (mee-RAHN-dah deh HA-noo-kah). Children are given special meat pies to thank them for helping others.

Sweet Israel Chicken

**Dotty Karo and
Cherie Karo Schwartz**

For over a thousand years, the Jewish people did not live in Israel, but they always longed to return to their "land of milk and honey." When the State of Israel was finally granted in 1948, they rededicated themselves to the land. They made the desert bloom again with the foods their ancestors had eaten: almonds and walnuts, apricots and grapes, olive oil, onions, and honey. This sweet chicken recipe, which includes many of the foods eaten at the first Hanukkah, was created by my family for holiday gatherings.

Variations on the Recipe:

You can use favorite dried fruits from your area in the recipe instead of the Israeli ones. Try dried apples, pears, or peaches. You can also use fresh or canned fruits like mandarin oranges, fruit cocktail, or fresh peaches, oranges, or tangerines.

You can also use other nuts, like cashews, pistachios, or hazelnuts.

INGREDIENTS FOR CHICKEN FOR 6 TO 8 PEOPLE:

3 pounds chicken, cut up

25 dried apricots (or apricots and prunes) quartered

4 ounces orange, apricot, or pomegranate preserves or marmalade

½ cup chopped walnuts or almonds

¼ cup olive oil

½ cup raisins

½ cup heavy grape juice, or sweet Concord grape or blackberry Kosher wine

1½ tablespoons vinegar

3 cloves garlic, minced

1 large onion, sliced thin

⅓ cup honey

DIRECTIONS:

1. Preheat the oven to 350 degrees F.

2. Rinse the chicken pieces and lay them in a large glass pan.

3. Combine the rest of the ingredients in a large bowl, and make sure that they are well mixed. Pour the mixture evenly over the chicken.

4. Bake the chicken in the oven for about 1½ hours, or until golden brown. About every 15 minutes while baking, spoon liquid over the chicken. Add water if necessary.

The Story of Benjamin

ADAPTED FROM THE CLASSIC MIDRASH

Not too far away from the city of Modi'in, the family of the Maccabees was anxiously awaiting the return of their cousin Judah. They had heard that the Temple had been saved from the enemy, and the people knew that there was much work to be done. The Seleucids had not taken care of the Temple. Now the Jews had to remove all of the idols and the altar and clean the whole Temple from top to bottom until it was holy once again! People were very eager to help restore the Temple so that they could worship in it.

Little Benjamin, the youngest in the group, stood watching while everyone gathered supplies and got ready to go to the Temple. Benjamin was only six years old, but he understood what had happened, and he wanted to help. The adults were so busy and moving so quickly that he didn't have the chance. He saw a broom standing by the wall and went over to get it, but an adult got to it before he could. He saw some old rags and reached for them, but bigger hands got them first.

"Benjamin, it is very nice that you want to help," said his mother, gently, "but this work is for grownups. You can help by staying out of the way."

So Benjamin stayed in the corner and watched all of the people in the house and in the streets run around busily. He started to pretend that he was one of the brave Maccabee soldiers, marching off to battle and coming home in victory. He was marching around in a circle, with his head held high, so he didn't even notice when the real soldiers came around a corner, and he bumped right into one of them. "Oh, look who's here!" one of the soldiers called, "a real Maccabee!" Benjamin felt so proud. The soldiers had called him a Maccabee! But then, he heard his mother calling.

"Benjamin! Benjamin! What are you doing? Getting in the way again? Come back over here and leave the soldiers alone."

"That's all right," said one of the soldiers. "We can't stay, anyway. We've come to take the supplies back to the Temple and to get more volunteers. Can any of you help?"

That was all that Benjamin needed to hear. "I can. I can help. I love to clean. Please let me come with you. I can clean really fast. I'll do a great job. Please?"

Benjamin's mother quickly came to his side. "We know that you want to help, Benjamin. Everyone wants to help clean the Temple. But the best help that you can be is to stay here out of the way so that we can finish our work."

Benjamin just looked at the ground. Then one of the soldiers spoke. He had a voice that sounded like gentle thunder. "I think that we might have just the right job for Benjamin at the Temple. We need someone who can distribute the brooms and hand out new rags to the workers. He could come with us. Would that be possible?"

Benjamin could hardly believe his ears. Here was this brave soldier giving him a real job! But then, he heard his mother's reply. "No, I'm afraid for him, Judah. There might still be enemy soldiers out there. He might get into everybody's way. I'm sorry, Benjamin."

That was Judah the Maccabee standing right in front of him! Judah had given him a job! He had to be able to go to the Temple with mighty Judah.

Judah the Maccabee spoke again. "There's really no danger now, and this young boy really wants to help. I promise that we will keep an eye on him. Let him come just for a little while, and I'll have the soldiers return him safe and sound."

There was silence for a long time—forever, it seemed to Benjamin. Then his mother said, "Since you have asked, Judah, I will have to say yes. But please promise me that you will watch him carefully and make sure that he doesn't get into trouble or in the way. Benjamin, you may go to the Temple."

And so, little Benjamin went away with the soldiers. He was so proud! He marched along with their big strides, trying to keep up with them and trying to look like a real soldier.

They walked for a long, long time, and Benjamin was starting to feel very tired. Finally, they turned a corner, and there it was—the beautiful Temple! Only now, it did not look very beautiful. There was dirt and dust everywhere. There were big, strange-looking statues lying in pieces on the ground and more standing in the Temple. Some people were dragging the statues outside, and others were cleaning the walls and floors. Just as Judah was showing Benjamin where the supplies were kept, he was called by some men working on the altar. He told the other workers, "This is Benjamin. Bring your dusty rags and brooms to him, and he will give you clean ones. He'll be a great help." When Benjamin looked up, Judah had disappeared into the crowds.

Many hours later, things were looking much better in the Temple. There was a new altar, the floors were clean, the broken stones had been replaced, and there was not a single statue anywhere in sight. Some of the workers had made a new Temple lamp out of the spears of the enemy soldiers. People were saying that the eternal light in the menorah should be rekindled to show that the Temple was with the Jewish people once again. Someone went to the storage room to find oil, but there was not even a single flask. They could not rededicate the Temple without lighting the menorah. Everyone started looking around the Temple, trying to find the sacred oil. It was getting very late in the day, but the search continued.

"Do not lose faith," cried Judah to the people. "We have cleaned and restored the Temple; now we must be able to rekindle the lights." When he mentioned the word "clean," Judah remembered a promise he had made to a certain mother about a certain young boy.

"Has anyone seen Benjamin? Does anyone know where he is?" Many people had seen him throughout the day, scurrying around, helping wherever he could, but no one had seen him in the last hour or so. "He's very young, just a boy. Doesn't anyone know where he is?" No one knew. And so, a search party was started, and the workers were calling Benjamin's name all over the Temple. But what if he had gone outside? What if something had happened to him?

"Quiet! I thought I heard something!" yelled one man who was outside of the Temple, standing by a hole in the wall surrounded by toppled stones. Everyone stopped searching, and it was quiet for the first time in hours. Everyone listened, and in the silence there it was: a weak cry from inside of the wall.

"Help!" It was Benjamin.

"Where are you? Inside that little crevice? How did you ever fit into that tiny space? Are you stuck? We can help you," the people cried. All at once, they began to gently remove stone after stone until finally, under all of the rubble, there was a very dusty, very frightened little Benjamin. They pulled him up and made sure that he was all right. Then they noticed that his left fist was closed tightly.

"What is the matter? Did you hurt your hand? Here, let's take a look. What were you doing under all of those stones?" Carefully, one old man opened Benjamin's fingers, and there, in his hand, was a small flask. Judah came over, took the bottle, and opened it in front of the people. Suddenly, a shout of joy rose up from everyone as they saw what the flask contained—oil!

"I'm sorry, Judah," said Benjamin. "I know that I should not have wandered away, but I saw the stones. No one else had looked there for the oil, and the space behind them was

too small for any of the grownups to explore, so I thought that I would just take a look. There was a little bottle of oil! I had to reach it, but the space was almost too small for me. Then I got stuck, and I called for help, but there was so much noise, and then. . . ."

"You are all right, Benjamin. You were the only one who could have fit into that tiny space. And you were certainly right about being able to help here today." Judah took the flask of oil, and as he held Benjamin's small hand, the two of them walked across the room to the Temple menorah. Judah carefully poured the oil into the cups. Then he lifted Benjamin high in the air so that he could light the sacred lamp. "The Holy Temple is rededicated this twenty-fifth day of Kislev. There is only enough oil for one day, but at least it is a start, a new beginning. And people, do you see? One small boy with one big wish to help was able to bring light to a whole people."

We know today that the light from that little bit of oil lasted for eight days! One little boy lit one little flame in the night, and there was light.

Mezuzah

**Dotty Karo and
Cherie Karo Schwartz**

One of the major themes of Hanukkah is rededication. In many countries and traditions, Hanukkah is the time to rededicate ourselves to Judaism by doing good deeds, helping others, and helping to repair the world. In Jewish homes, a mezuzah is hung on the doorposts as a reminder of the commandments. A mezuzah is a small cylinder that contains prayers important to Judaism. Making a new mezuzah for your home for Hanukkah is a good way to rededicate yourself. A mezuzah can be made from many materials and in many shapes.

MATERIALS:

flour

salt

water

*different-colored paints,
markers, and/or glitter
sticks*

two small nails

masking tape

*mezuzah paper or
parchment that is inserted
into the back of the
mezuzah (this may be
purchased from a Judaica
or synagogue gift shop)*

INSTRUCTIONS:

1. Decide on a shape for your mezuzah. (See examples shown to get some ideas.) You may want to draw your design on paper before making it out of dough.

2. Create a dough from two parts flour, one part salt, and enough water to make the mixture workable. Start with ½ cup flour, ¼ cup salt, and 2 tablespoons water, and add more water if you need it.

In Libya, the <u>gabbai</u> (GAH-by) of the synagogue (the person who makes sure that all words of Torah read are properly pronounced) is called up to the Torah for special recognition on the first day of Hanukkah. The congregation then thanks him for his dedicated work.

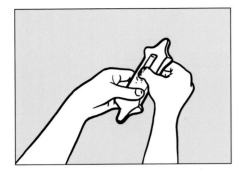

3. Take some of the dough and make the shape of the mezuzah. You need to make the mezuzah out of one piece of dough, or it may come apart as it dries. Most mezuzahs are long and barrel-shaped, and some have ridges, points, or rounded edges. With your thumb, hollow out a space in the back big enough to hold the mezuzah parchment.

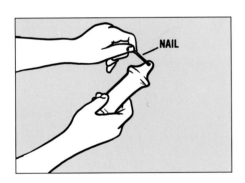

4. Make a small hole at the bottom and at the top of the mezuzah with one of the nails so that the mezuzah can be hung up when it is complete.

5. Set the mezuzah aside to dry, which will take a day or two. If you would like it to dry sooner, ask an adult to help you place it on a baking sheet in a 250-degree-F oven for about 15 minutes.

6. After it is dry, paint the mezuzah with designs, such as flowers, animals, shapes, Jewish symbols, or Hebrew words. A traditional mezuzah has a Hebrew letter *shin* on the front, so you may want to add that to your design.

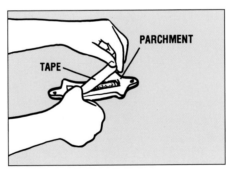

7. After the paint has dried, place the rolled parchment inside the back of the mezuzah. Hold the parchment in place with a small piece of tape across the back opening.

8. Hang your mezuzah somewhere in your house. It can go on the door frame of the front

or back door of the house, or on the door frame of a room. The mezuzah is placed about one-third of the way down the frame, on the right side of the door as you enter, and it is slanted with the top inclined toward the room.

Three Hanukkah Haikus

Larry Schwartz and Cherie Karo Schwartz

Each Hanukkah night
we rededicate our lives.
A candle glows on.

Rededication:
helping re-create the world
in a better light.

Miraculous oil
Flowing to flickering flames;
Dedication shines.

CHAPTER SIX

Miracles

In our modern world, with all of its science and technology, it may not be easy to believe in miracles anymore. But look around you. There are thousands of miracles every day. It is a miracle that the sun comes up each morning. It is a miracle that sometimes we get just the right help that we need. It is a miracle that flowers open in the sun, that rain comes so the trees can grow, and that stars come out at night. If we really stop to think, we may figure out explanations for what has happened, but they certainly are still miracles.

There are many miracles in Jewish history. It was a miracle that the Temple was saved by the Maccabees. It was a miracle that the small army of the Maccabees was able to defeat a huge, powerful enemy. In more ancient times, it was miraculous that the Jews were able to flee ancient Egypt. In modern times, it is a miracle that the Jewish people finally regained their homeland with the rebirth of Israel in 1948. It is also miraculous that the Ethiopian Jews who were starving were saved by a remarkable airlift called "Operation Moses." And after years of oppression and of waiting, Russian Jews were finally allowed to emigrate to the United States and Israel. We are thankful for these many miracles.

In Israel, it is a miracle that the Jewish people were able to turn a desert land into a land of "milk and honey" again. The Israelis invented an irrigation system that brings water to the desert. Because of the care they have given the land, they can now grow many foods that once grew in ancient Israel, some of which had not grown there for a thousand years! People say that the Jews have been miracle workers in the desert.

In some ways, Hanukkah is all about miracles. It was a miracle that the Maccabees defeated the people who did not allow them to worship as they chose. And it was a miracle that one tiny vial of oil was found in the Temple, and that it burned for eight days until new oil could be made. Some scholars say that

Hanukkah Miracles

Story of Hanukkah
Of miracles and light,
Story of light shining
In the darkest night.

Tiny band of Jews
Mattathias and sons five
Fighting a huge army,
Keeping faith alive.

One can overcome much
Wrong defeated by right;
The darkest night is broken
By one tiny light.

One single person
Who believes it so
Can still see the miracles
As in days long ago.

One little candle,
One little light
Sends out a message
In the darkest night.

"HaNerot Halalu"
from liturgy

הַנֵּרוֹת הַלָּלוּ אֲנַחְנוּ מַדְלִיקִין
עַל הַנִּסִּים וְעַל הַתְּשׁוּעוֹת וְעַל
הַנִּפְלָאוֹת שֶׁעָשִׂיתָ לַאֲבוֹתֵינוּ בַּיָּמִים
הָהֵם בַּזְּמַן הַזֶּה עַל יְדֵי כֹּהֲנֶיךָ
הַקְּדוֹשִׁים. וְכָל שְׁמוֹנַת יְמֵי חֲנֻכָּה

הַנֵּרוֹת הַלָּלוּ קֹדֶשׁ הֵם וְאֵין
לָנוּ רְשׁוּת לְהִשְׁתַּמֵּשׁ בָּהֶם אֶלָּא
לִרְאוֹתָם בִּלְבָד כְּדֵי לְהוֹדוֹת
לְשִׁמְךָ הַגָּדוֹל עַל־נִסֶּיךָ וְעַל־
יְשׁוּעָתֶךָ וְעַל נִפְלְאוֹתֶיךָ.

HaNerot halalu anachnu madlikin

al hanisim v'al hat'shu-ot

v'al hanifla-ot she-asita la-avoteynu
  bayamim

haheym baz'man hazeh al y'dey
  kohanecha

hak'doshim.

We kindle these lights,

For the miracles and wonders

For the redemption

That You performed for our ancestors

Through Your holy priests

In those days at that time.

These lights are sacred

Throughout the eight days of Hanukkah;

We are not permitted to make

Any other use of them

Except watching them,

In order to praise Your great name

For Your miracles

Your wonders

And Your triumphs.

Hanukkah was celebrated for many years after the Seleucid war, but that for some time it was almost forgotten. The Rabbis in the first two centuries CE (the Common Era) restored the holiday's importance. Perhaps it is a miracle that Hanukkah is once again celebrated.

The miracles of Hanukkah are celebrated around the world in very special ways. One of the most well-known of the Hanukkah symbols is the dreidel, a four-sided top. There is a Hebrew letter on each side of the dreidel: *nun, gimel, hey, shin.* They are the first letters of the words *Nes gadol haya sham,* which means "A great miracle happened there," a reminder of the Hanukkah story. The dreidels in Israel have a Hebrew letter *pey,* which stands for "here," so the phrase is "A great miracle happened here." Why the difference? Because the miracle of Hanukkah happened in the Land of Israel!

Long ago in Germany and other European countries, the last night of Hanukkah was a special night to remember the miracle of the light. A huge bonfire was built, and all the leftover wicks and oil from the people's hanukkiyot were added to it. The people sang and danced around the fire long into the night.

But the greatest miracle is that the Jewish people have continued to survive—despite all odds and enemies—and to have faith, and that the Jews continue to help bring light into the world. May the miracles continue!

On Hanukkah each year, Syrian Jewish parents give each of their children a candle in the shape of a hand, called a hamsa (HAHM-sah), to protect them and to "keep away the evil eye," bringing a miracle of protection.

In the Sephardic communities, the hanukkiya is placed on or near a window so that everyone can remember the miracle of light.

In the late 1940s the Jews of Yemen had most of their freedoms taken away. In 1949 and 1950, almost 50,000 Jews were taken by airplanes to Israel on "Operation Magic Carpet." The Torah states, "I will redeem you on the wings of eagles." These Jews had never seen airplanes before, and thought they were silver eagles!

In Aden, Yemen, the children used to wear blue clothing on Hanukkah, because blue is the color of the heavens, and miracles come from heaven. In school, they re-created the winning battle of the Maccabees as a reminder of that miracle.

Neyyapam

Cherie Karo Schwartz

In Jewish households around the world, foods made with oil are eaten to commemorate the miracle of the tiny vial of oil found in the Temple. In Southern India, the Jewish community enjoys these fried cakes called neyyapam (nay-ah-PAHM.) The story of how the Jews of the Bene Israel community got to India is a kind of Hanukkah miracle, too. A group of Jews fled Israel in the second century BCE and were shipwrecked off the coast of India. Miraculously, they survived and settled south of Bombay.

Be sure to ask an adult to help you fry the cakes.

INGREDIENTS FOR NEYYAPAM FOR 4 TO 6 PEOPLE:

2 cups water

½ cup sugar

⅛ teaspoon salt

1 cup semolina

1 cup flour

1 tablespoon sesame seeds

¼ cup chopped almonds or almonds and cashews

¼ cup chopped dried fruits, like apricots, raisins, and dates

¼ teaspoon ground cardamom

½ teaspoon baking powder

enough vegetable oil for deep frying (about 2 inches in the bottom of a pan)

DIRECTIONS:

1. Mix the water, sugar, and salt in a pot on the stove, and let it come to a boil. Remove from the stove and let cool to room temperature.

2. Add the semolina, flour, seeds, nuts, and fruits to the sugar water, and mix. Cover and let stand at room temperature overnight.

3. The next day, add the cardamom and baking powder and stir well.

4. Have an adult help you from now on. Heat a large skillet on medium heat, and add the oil.

5. When the oil is hot, drop large spoonfuls of dough into the skillet and fry, turning occasionally, until golden brown, about 4 minutes. (Oil is hot when you can add a drop of water to the oil and it sizzles.)

6. Remove the cakes and drain them on paper towels.

The Hanukkah Visitor

FROM THE EGYPTIAN FOLKTALE

Once in Egypt there lived a poor widow with seven young children. They barely had enough food from day to day, but they all worked together to make a living by doing small jobs in the community. One year, as the time of Hanukkah grew close, the family found that there were very few jobs to do, and there was little money. All of the children were sad and hungry.

On the day before the first night of Hanukkah, all of the children sat with their mother and tried to cheer each other up. "Well, even if we do not get any special Hanukkah things this year, we can at least have the delicious Hanukkah pancakes, right, Mother?" one child asked. The mother just looked at her good children. She did not have the heart to tell them that she did not even have enough money to buy flour for the pancakes.

Instead she said, "Well, children, we cannot make pancakes in dirty pots! I will go to the river and give them all a good cleaning. You can stay here and clean the house for the holiday." The children all smiled as they watched their mother walk down to the river. Then they started to clean the whole house. While they worked, they talked about how sweet and good the Hanukkah pancakes would be!

Their mother walked slowly toward the river. How could she tell her children that they would not have any pancakes? She could not get any flour.

When the mother reached the river, she stopped and watched it flowing past. How she wished that the children's father were still alive. How she missed the days when the whole family had beautiful holiday celebrations together. How she would miss the Hanukkah pancakes and joy! But she thought of her beautiful children, and that made her a little happier.

The mother sat by the river and thought, "We can at least have very clean pots!" and she began scrubbing the biggest pot as hard as she could. She rubbed it until it shone!

Suddenly, she noticed a reflection in the pot, and she turned to find an old man standing next to her. He had on a long black coat, and he carried an old walking stick. "Can I help you?" she asked, surprised.

"Peace be to you," the old man answered. "I am a stranger here, and I do not know anyone in this town. Tomorrow is Hanukkah, and I have no place to stay and no one to celebrate the holiday with. Could I come and share the candle lighting with you?"

Without even thinking, the woman said, "Of course you can! A guest is an honor and a delight! My children and I live right over that hill, and we would be happy to have your company!"

"Amen and amen," responded the old man. "So let it be!"

When the woman turned around to tell the stranger where her house was, the old man had disappeared. He must have already headed up the hill, she thought. Then she remembered. "How could I have told that nice man that he could celebrate Hanukkah with us? We do not even have enough money to buy flour! Oh, what a sad, sad day!"

The mother went back to her cleaning, and before long, all of the pots were shiny. She gathered them up and slowly made her way back to her house. As she headed up the hill, the woman thought, "Oh, dear! What will I tell my children? What will I tell our guest?"

As she approached, her children came running up to greet her with smiles and laughter. "Oh, my sweet children! What makes you so happy?"

"Don't you know? Your friend came by while you were gone!"

"Friend? What friend?"

"Don't tease us, dear Mama! Your friend with the long black coat and the walking stick was here. And look at what he brought: so many coins, oil for our hanukkiya, and even a great big sack of flour! What a wonderful surprise! What a wonderful friend!"

"And where is he now?" asked the mother as she looked around the house.

"He said that he couldn't stay," explained the children, "but he left these things here."

The mother looked at all of the holiday surprises and smiled. She said a little prayer of thanks and then spoke to her family. "Come, children! We have so much work to do! See the clean pots? Now we have to clean the hanukkiya until it shines like gold!"

The woman and her seven children spent all the next day cleaning house, buying food, and, of course, frying many delicious pancakes.

And all through Hanukkah, even though they bought a great many things, the money did not run out. Even though they made many, many pancakes, enough for all of their neighbors as well as for themselves, the dough never ran out. And, the oil for the hanukkiya was enough to last for all eight nights of Hanukkah!

On the last night of the holiday, the children, filled with pancakes and stories and joy, gathered around their mother. "But what happened to your friend, Mama? Why didn't he ever come back for the wonderful pancakes and to help us celebrate Hanukkah? Who was he, Mama?"

The mother hugged her children and looked into their happy faces. And then she told them: "That was a very special friend, children, one whom you will always want to remember. And his name is Elijah [ee-LIE-ja]. His story is told wherever there are Jewish people. He is a prophet of old, the one who appears in many disguises and in many places to help those who are in need and who will use his gifts wisely and well. And we were blessed by his company! Amen and amen, so let it be."

"Al Hanisim"
"The Miracles"
from liturgy

עַל הַנִסִּים וְעַל הַפֻּרְקָן וְעַל
הַגְבוּרוֹת וְעַל הַתְּשׁוּעוֹת שֶׁעָשִׂיתָ
לַאֲבוֹתֵינוּ בַּיָּמִים הָהֵם בַּזְּמַן הַזֶּה;

בִּימֵי מַתִּתְיָהוּ בֶּן־יוֹחָנָן כֹּהֵן גָּדוֹל
חַשְׁמוֹנָאִי וּבָנָיו כְּשֶׁעָמְדָה מַלְכוּת יָוָן
עַל עַמְּךָ יִשְׂרָאֵל לְהַשְׁכִּיחָם תּוֹרָתֶךָ
וּלְהַעֲבִירָם מֵחֻקֵּי רְצוֹנֶךָ:

עַל הַנִסִּים וְעַל הַפֻּרְקָן . . .

וְאַתָּה בְּרַחֲמֶיךָ הָרַבִּים עָמַדְתָּ לָהֶם
בְּעֵת צָרָתָם.

עַל הַנִסִּים וְעַל הַפֻּרְקָן . . .

Al hanisim v'al hapurkan v'al hag'vurot v'al hat'shuot

She-asita la-avoteynu bayamim haheym baz'man hazeh:

Bimey Matityahu ben Yochanan koheyn gadol

Hashmonai uvanav k'she-amdah malchut

Yavan al amcha Yisrael

L'hashkicham toratecha

Ul'ha-aviram meychukey r'tsonecha:

V'atah b'rachamecha harabim amad'ta lahem b'eyt tsaratam.

We thank You for the miracles, for the triumphant victories,

And for the deliverance of our ancestors in olden days at this season.

It happened in the days of Mattathias, son of Yochanan the High Priest,

The Hasmonean and his sons.

The cruel power of the Seleucids rose up against the people of Israel

demanding that they abandon Your Torah and violate Your laws.

And You in Your great mercy stood by Your people in their time of trouble.

Hanukkah Hamsa Candle

The tradition of the hamsa (HAHM-sah) candle comes from Syria. The people of the Middle East, Jews and Arabs, have believed for hundreds of years that the hamsa, a wax candle made in the shape of a hand, is a kind of miracle-protection from harm. Jewish children in Syria are given these candles at Hanukkah. Middle Eastern Jews associate the hamsa with Hanukkah because they remember the miracle of finding safety in other Middle Eastern countries after they were expelled from Spain in 1492. The candle combines the miracle of protection with the miracle of light.

Please make sure that an adult helps with this project.

The Moroccan hanukkiya has five representations of hands (hamsas) and two doves that point the way to the shammash (guard) on top of the oil holders, in remembrance of the miracles of Hanukkah. Some Moroccan Jews are descendants of Jews who were expelled from Spain in 1492 and who miraculously found safety in Morocco.

MATERIALS:

4 blocks (one pound) paraffin wax for candle-making or canning

colored crayon

6 inches heavy waxed string or candle wick

9- to 10-inch round cake pan

double boiler, or metal coffee can placed in a large pan of water

a piece of paper

pencil

scissors

table knife

INSTRUCTIONS:

1. Place three of the wax blocks in the upper part of double boiler or coffee can. Place water in the lower half of double boiler, or in a pan if you are using a coffee can. Set the can in the pan of water. If you are making a colored candle, add half of a crayon to the wax.

2. Heat the wax on high heat on the stove until the blocks are completely melted, about 12 to 15 minutes. Stir the melted wax and crayon so that the color mixes evenly. The crayon may take longer to melt.

3. Have an adult remove the pot from the burner and then remove the container with the wax from the pot. Have the adult pour the hot wax very

carefully into the cake pan and set the pan aside to cool (about 30 to 40 minutes).

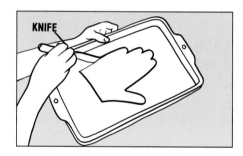

4. While the wax is cooling, trace an outline of your hand on a piece of paper and carefully cut out the shape.

5. When the wax has cooled to semisoft, place your hand-pattern on top of the wax and, using a knife, cut around the hand shape.

6. Remove the paper pattern and the outside wax pieces from the pan and set them aside.

7. Take the last block of wax, and gently push it against the bottom of the hamsa candle, lifting the hand slightly so it sits in the middle of the block. Hold the block to the hamsa until it is securely in place. In about 10 minutes, the two pieces should stick together.

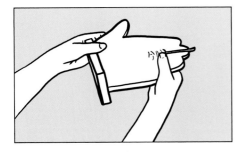

8. Stand the hamsa candle upright so that you can see that it will stay together and stand. Make a shallow groove, around ¼ inch deep, on the back side of the candle along the middle finger. Place the wick in the groove so that a piece about 1 inch long is sticking up above the candle. Then gently press the wax back together to cover up the wick.

9. After you have finished attaching the wick, set the candle back flat into the pan to cool.

10. Use your fingers to round and shape the fingers and the rest of the wax hand along the cut edge.

11. Keep the candle in the pan until it has completely cooled (at least a few hours). If you stand it up before it cools, it will lose its shape.

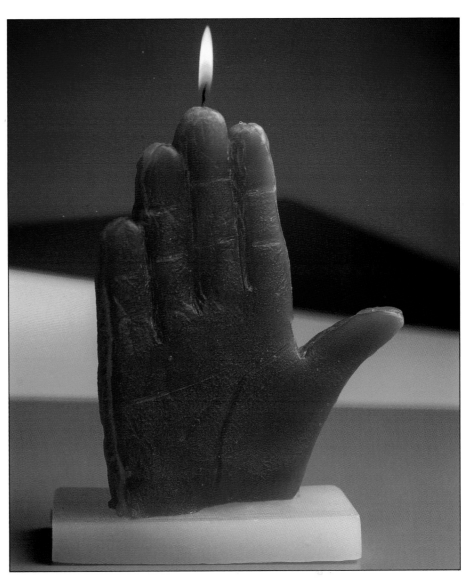

Miracles of Old, Miracles to Come

Every Hanukkah night
the story's always told
of many miracles
done in days of old.

The Hasmoneans strong
in caves hidden away
fought and won their freedom
so we'd be free today.

The victories they won then
were miracles, it's true,
and miracles of light
were shown with the oil, too.

But the greatest miracle
that could now come to be
would be a time of peace,
joy and tranquility.

CHAPTER SEVEN

Hope

Look at the candles burning so brightly in the hanukkiya on the last night of Hanukkah. What a beautiful sight! You watch them until the very last candle burns all the way down. Then there is a small puff of smoke. In the candles and the puff of smoke is the hope that there will always be light in the world. With the passing of each Hanukkah comes the hope that there will be a celebration the next year. And just like the last candle, this section of the book is about hope.

Hope is the central theme of Hanukkah. At the time of Mattathias, no matter what was taken away from the Jewish people, they refused to give up their faith or their hope. The sacrifices and the harsh rules made by King Antiochus IV only made the Jewish people believe more strongly in themselves and in their right to practice their own religion. They always hoped that someday they could return to worship in their own way in their own Temple.

The family of brave Mattathias knew that they were right in their beliefs, but they could only hope that the other Jews would follow them. They did! The tiny army of Jewish people living in the caves of Modi'in and fighting the whole enemy army could only hope that they could win. They did! Because of their hope and their faith, we are celebrating Hanukkah today.

The Jewish people have lived all over the world for thousands of years. Hope has helped to keep the Jews alive in many places during many trying times. In fifteenth-century Spain, the Jews were forced to leave their country, and they hoped to find a safe country in which to live. They moved to Greece, Syria, Morocco, Turkey, and many other countries. The Jews in Eastern Europe from the end of the 1800s up until World War II almost lost hope of surviving, but many did escape to the land of hope, America.

Hope is what gave strength and courage to our great Jewish leaders, such as Judith. According to legend, she lived a long

"Hatikvah"
**words by Naphtali Herz Imber;
English by Israel Zangwill**

כָּל עוֹד בַּלֵּבָב פְּנִימָה
נֶפֶשׁ יְהוּדִי הוֹמִיָּה,
וּלְפַאֲתֵי מִזְרָח קָדִימָה
עַיִן לְצִיּוֹן צוֹפִיָּה,
עוֹד לֹא אָבְדָה תִּקְוָתֵנוּ
הַתִּקְוָה מִשְּׁנוֹת אַלְפַּיִם,
לִהְיוֹת עַם חָפְשִׁי בְּאַרְצֵנוּ,
בְּאֶרֶץ צִיּוֹן וִירוּשָׁלַיִם.

Kol od baleyvav p'nimah
Nefesh y'hudi homiyah,
Ul'fa'atey mizrach kadimah
Ayin l'tsion tsofiyah,
Od lo av'da tikvateynu
hatikvah mishnot alpayim,
lih'yot am chofshi b'artseynu,
b'erets tsion virushalayim.

So long as still within our breasts
the Jewish heart beats true,
So long as still toward the East
To Zion, looks the Jew;
So long as our hopes are not yet
    lost—
Two thousand years we cherished
    them—
To live in freedom in the land
Of Zion and Jerusalem

Nine Candles

**Inspired by a poem by
Lisa Rauchwerger**

Nine wicks, curving toward the light,
Nine flames, flickering in the night,
Nine tiny lights waving to and fro,
Nine sparks of hope sending out their
    glow.

One tiny flame at the edge of its cup
One drop of wax before it's used up;
It' neighbor flickers in the deep
And then it sighs and nods to sleep.

The shammash has fallen asleep inside.
The others are resting; now they hide.
One gives a last breath, then a sigh
And a wisp of smoke rises high.

Now they have almost gone away
Nine points of light that shone today.
They were here for just one night
To show their beauty and their light.

They were all so colorfully bright
Filling the room with warm glowing
    light.
As they grow small, a hope lingers on
That light will return with the coming
    dawn.

Hope in the candles all in a row,
Hope for the miracles of long ago,
Hope for the children watching the
    light,
Hope from a candle alive in the night.

time ago and was a very brave woman. The enemy general Holofernes (ho-loh-FER-nees) was defeating the Jewish soldiers, and had already killed Judith's husband, but she did not give up hope. She dressed in beautiful clothes and went into the enemy camp to Holofernes. He thought she was very beautiful, and he invited her to eat with him. She offered him her own foods: very salty cheese and strong wine. When Holofernes had eaten the cheese, he got very thirsty, drank too much wine, and fell asleep. Then Judith took a sword and chopped off his head, saving the Jewish people! In Judith's honor, many Jewish communities around the world honor women on Hanukkah. The women are given special privileges, have special meals together, and tell stories of Judith and other strong women in Jewish history.

We learn about hope from the heroes who came before us, people like the leader Mattathias, Judah the Maccabee, and brave Judith. Their hope gave them strength, and we honor their hope on Hanukkah.

In many Jewish communities of the world, foods made with cheese are eaten on Hanukkah in honor of Judith. Some popular cheese foods are latkes made with cottage cheese, cheese kugel, cheese in pastry, and cheesecake.

In Eastern Europe, the women do not have to work on the first or the last nights of Hanukkah, in remembrance of Judith.

In North Africa in the past, on the seventh night of Hanukkah, the women went to the synagogue and, for the only time during the year, they could take the Torah scrolls from the ark and hold them.

In the city of Hebron in Israel, there is a celebration on the last night of Hanukkah. The women eat macaroni and salty cheese, and they spend the evening together talking and telling each other stories.

"Hatikvah" is the national anthem of Israel. The word hatikvah means "the hope." The words were written in 1878 by the poet Naphtali Herz Imber, and Samuel Cohen wrote the music. In the early 1900s, the song became the Zionist national anthem. In 1948, "Hatikvah" became the national anthem of Israel. The song tells of the hope that Israel will remain a free nation, and it is sung by Jewish people throughout the world.

Tiropita

Tiropita (tir-OH-pee-tah), Greek cheese pie, is an easy and delicious dish that uses one of the traditional Hanukkah foods: cheese. Eating cheese remembers and honors Judith for her hope and bravery, when she killed General Holofernes.

There are other versions of cheese pie made by other peoples of the Middle East, like the *bourek* (BOO-rek) in Turkey.

INGREDIENTS FOR TIROPITA FOR 10 TO 12 PEOPLE:

1 cup grated kasseri or other light white cheese, such as Monterey Jack

1 pound crumbled feta cheese

3 large eggs (or 5 egg whites)

½ cup melted margarine (or half margarine and half olive oil)

2 tablespoons chopped parsley

salt and pepper to taste

½ pound phyllo dough

TO MAKE TIROPITA:

1. Mix the two cheeses, eggs, and 3 tablespoons of the melted margarine together with the parsley and salt and pepper.

2. Preheat oven to 375 degrees F.

3. Gently unroll the phyllo leaves from the package, and lay the stack of phyllo leaves flat. You may want to cover the stack of phyllo with a slightly damp cloth as you work with one sheet at a time, so that the rest do not dry out.

4. Brush the bottom of a 10 × 15 inch glass baking pan with a thin layer of the remaining margarine (or margarine/olive oil mixture).

5. Carefully place one sheet of the phyllo dough in the bottom of the pan, curling the edges up on the sides of the pan. Brush the phyllo with margarine, then add another leaf of phyllo, and continue until there are five leaves of phyllo in the pan.

6. Fill the pan with the cheese mixture, and then repeat the process of adding five sheets of phyllo to the top of the mixture, brushing each sheet with margarine. Brush the top layer with margarine, too.

7. With the help of an adult, use a sharp knife to trim the extra phyllo dough around the top of the pan.

8. Place the pan in the oven and bake for 30 minutes, or until phyllo is golden brown.

The Light in the Window

AN EASTERN EUROPEAN FOLKTALE RECORDED BY DOV NOY FOR THE ISRAEL FOLKTALE ARCHIVES BY DAVID HACOHEN

Once, in the middle of a cold and snowy winter night in Eastern Europe, a farming family was gathered around the big, black wood stove in their cozy house. They were telling each other stories but then Poppa said something that the youngest, little Gittel, thought was very, very strange. "I hope that the snow stops in time for us to make the trip tomorrow," he said. Trip? In this great storm? How could anyone want to go out in such terrible weather? And tomorrow is the first night of Hanukkah!

Poppa noticed that little Gittel looked confused, so he explained, "Tomorrow we will all go to our neighbor Alexis' house. This year you are old enough to stay awake, and you will hear a lovely story that you will hear again and again for years to come. The rest is a surprise."

"Oh, Poppa, I love surprises!" said Gittel.

For the rest of the evening, the family got ready for Hanukkah. Everyone was busy. They took out the pots and pans for making delicious potato latkes, and the children took out their dreidels. Yosef, the oldest brother, carved a new wooden dreidel for Gittel, and drew the letters that stood for "a great miracle happened there." The girls polished the beautiful silver Hanukkah menorah with the long, curving branches until it shone like the moon. Then the children went off to bed. Momma and Poppa looked out the window at the lovely still scene and they both smiled.

The next morning, the sun rose brilliantly and made the whole countryside look as if it were covered with sparkling gems. The children were very excited when they ran outside to play after their chores. "I don't know how it happens, but there is always good weather for this very special day," said Momma later in the morning. "And now it is time to make the latkes." The older brothers went to the cellar for the vegetables. Then everybody peeled potatoes and grated onions in preparation for the best latkes in town.

The day passed quickly, and soon the sun began to set over the far hills. "Come on children! Get your coats, hats, and gloves, and bring the tray of latkes," called Poppa. "We can't be late, and we have a long walk to Alexis' house."

"But Poppa," asked Gittel, "why are we going all the way to Alexis' house on the first night of Hanukkah? He isn't even Jewish."

"You will hear the story from Alexis when we get there, I promise," said Momma as she wrapped little Gittel's coat closer around her and gave her a hug. "Just be patient."

And so, the whole family made their way, with their neighbors, across the snow-covered countryside toward Alexis' farm. This made Gittel even more curious. All of the neighbors were talking and laughing with each other, and each family had brought some food. It seemed as if the whole town were going to visit Alexis.

Finally, they arrived at the farm, and Alexis welcomed them warmly to his small house. "Happy Hanukkah! Happy Hanukkah! Oh, my goodness! How nice you all look. Look at all this food. And look at all the wonderful children. Come in, come in. Go and get nice and warm by the fireplace."

Soon, all the people had had their fill of delicious foods, including the best latkes in town. Then Alexis called them all together in the living room. "Well," he began. His voice was so low that everyone stayed very quiet so that they could hear him. "I guess that it is time to tell my tale. Hanukkah is a time of miracles, but not just from the past. We must always hope that they will continue to happen. We have to tell the story. Who hasn't heard it yet? Gittel? Moishe? Sari? Come closer to the story, and closer to the fire, dears. Please listen to an old man's tale." And so Alexis began . . .

"Once, many years ago, there was a huge snowstorm, much like the one we had yesterday. I was living alone, just as I live now. I could see that big snowstorm coming. I knew that the horses and cows would need food, so I went out to the barn to get them some hay. Then I remembered that I was almost out of firewood, so I headed for the woods. There were no good trees close by, and I kept thinking that if I went a little bit farther, I would find all that I'd need. It was bitter cold, the snow was whirling around and around, and I couldn't even see my hand in front of my face. In just a few minutes, the beautiful snow had turned into a stormy nightmare. I had lost my sense of direction, walking this way and that, and soon I was hopelessly lost.

"Now, you might think that it is very silly for a grown man to lose his way right next to his house. Please understand how easy it is to lose your direction in a swirling snowstorm. I was very scared. I could feel my toes growing numb inside my big leather boots. I knew that I had to keep moving to stay warm, but I didn't know where I was going. What if I couldn't find my house? Then, I realized that I had been standing still. I couldn't do that or I would freeze. What was I to do? How would I ever find my way back home? I was so very tired, and I knew there was no hope of being rescued."

Alexis stopped talking. The room was absolutely still. The only sound was the crackling of the fire in the fireplace. The children watched the flames changing shapes and looked at the shadows on the wall. Then they looked back at Alexis as he continued.

"As I trudged through the storm, a big gust of wind pushed the swirling snow aside, and I saw a tree in front of me. The trunk looked so inviting, just the place to take a rest. I stopped for a moment to catch my breath. I sat down in the snow and leaned up against the tree. And then I closed my eyes."

"Wake up! Don't die, Mr. Alexis! Don't die!" cried Gittel. She got up and threw her arms around the man.

"Don't worry, little one," soothed Alexis, as he patted her soft, red hair. "I'm here to tell the story, aren't I?" Gittel nodded her head, and the older children laughed.

"So there I was on the ground, all thought of hope gone, when all of a sudden, something made me open my eyes. Off in the distance, I saw a little light. No, I thought; I must be dreaming. I rubbed my eyes and looked again. Could there be hope? I stood up, and I started walking slowly toward the light.

"Each step that I took was such an effort. I was so cold and tired. But each step that I took also brought me closer to the tiny light getting larger in my view. Soon I could see that it was actually two little lights in a window. Finally, I came to the door of a house. I knocked as loudly as I could.

"A farmer and his young son came to the door. 'Don't cry! Your tears will freeze!'" I looked up, and there was Berel, one of the neighbor boys. He and his father helped me into their nice warm house, and I was saved. They sat me down in front of the fire, put blankets around me, and gave me some warm, delicious soup."

Gittel, who had been listening so carefully to the whole story, suddenly cried out, "Berel? That was the boy? That's Poppa's name, too!"

The rest of the family looked at little Gittel, and Momma hugged her and said, "That's right, dear. His name is Berel."

Then Alexis continued. "After I began to warm up, there was one thing I wanted to know. 'The strangest thing happened while I was out there in the storm. I had almost given up all hope of surviving when, suddenly, I thought I saw a light. I followed it, and it led me here. What was it?'

"'Turn around and see for yourself,' said the farmer. There was a silver candleholder with nine curving branches, and two flickering candles.

"'It's beautiful!' I said. 'But what is it, and why do you put it in the window?'

"'It's our Hanukkah menorah,' explained young Berel. 'Tonight is the first night of Hanukkah, so we have one candle plus the shammes.' Then Berel told me the whole Hanukkah tale, as I sat being warmed by the fire and by the beauty of the story.

"I stayed with the family for the night, and the next morning the sun rose beautiful and bright, just like this morning. Then Berel and his father led me back to my home. 'I don't know how I can ever thank you,' I told them. 'You saved my life. Your menorah was a miracle for me.'

"I promised myself then and there that I would never forget, and I haven't. I'm not Jewish, but I have never forgotten Hanukkah. Every year I tell my story. A candle in the dark restored my hope and saved my life, and now I light candles of hope with you."

Alexis stopped talking. Many of the neighbors had tears in their eyes. Everyone was smiling. The fire had burned down low, and the snow glistened outside the window as Alexis lit the candles and everyone recited the prayers for the first night of Hanukkah.

Then Gittel spoke up. "What a beautiful story. The Hanukkah menorah in the story was so pretty, almost like ours. And the boy's name in the story was Berel, just like Poppa. But Poppa isn't a little boy. He's a Poppa!"

Everyone started laughing. Momma and Poppa's eyes were glistening. Poppa lifted Gittel up into his strong, safe arms as Alexis said gently, "Your Poppa is all grown up now, but I can still see his young face at the door that night. Such a young face, so full of hope."

Clay Hanukkiya

In ancient Israel, the only lights people had were oil lamps. Small lamps made out of clay were used throughout the land. When the holiday of Hanukkah was developed, the first hanukkiyot were made of clay, too. The hanukkiya is the major symbol of the holiday of hope. The Maccabees were the hope for the Jewish people. They fought so that they could return to light the menorah in the great Temple again, and by their faith and hope, they succeeded. Today archaeologists all over Israel find thousands of oil lamps made of clay in archaeological digs. Here are instructions for you to make your own clay hanukkiya that you can use for Hanukkah.

Hope is something that has helped keep the Jewish people alive. In ancient Israel, it was each Jewish person's duty to go to Jerusalem. In modern times, many Jews hope to go to Israel, and every year, thousands of Jewish people around the world fulfill that hope. Many people go to Israel to visit, and many others decide to return to live in the land of our hope, Israel. Traditionally, people say, "Next Year in Jerusalem."

MATERIALS:

1 pound self-hardening clay

large sheet of heavy plastic

small bowl of water

plastic knife

Hanukkah candles

different-colored paints

INSTRUCTIONS:

1. Find a picture in a book to use as a model for your hanukkiya, or be creative and draw your own. It can be any shape you wish, as long as it has holes for eight candles in a row and one candle up higher for the shammash. The hanukkiya can have decorations of Jewish or personal symbols, and it can be made of nine separate candleholders or as one piece. Use your imagination and come up with a hanukkiya design that is yours.

2. Work the clay with your hands until you can mold it easily.

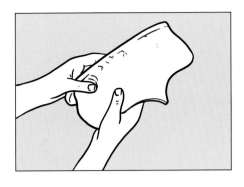

3. Using your hands and the knife, break the clay into two pieces, one for the base and one for the back. Mold the shape and size of the flat base, and set it aside. Take a second piece of clay and mold it into the back. Attach the back piece to the base by wetting your fingers and pressing the two pieces together.

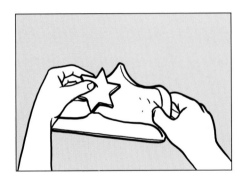

4. Mold decorations and shapes, and add them to your hanukkiya. Wet your fingers, touch each piece, and then press the two pieces together.

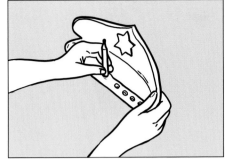

5. Use candles as models for the size and shape of the nine candleholders. Decide where you want the candles to stand, and press them into their places one at a time. Be sure you don't push them through the bottom of the base. Make sure you turn the candles around in the holes so that they are a little loose. They will fit after the hanukkiya dries.

6. When your hanukkiya shape is finished, wet your fingers well and gently rub down the whole outside of the hanukkiya until it is smooth.

7. You can dry your hanukkiya in one of two ways. You can set it aside to dry. (It is dry when it turns a lighter color and is no longer cool to the touch.) Or you can have an adult help you set it on a piece of aluminum foil and place it in a 250-degree-F oven for about 15 minutes.

8. Once your hanukkiya is completely dry, paint it either a solid color or many different colors.

Hanukkah Hopes

Can you remember when you look into the night

And see your neighbors' Hanukkah lights?

How brightly they burn in the window with care

How flames glow in darkness to show they were there?

Seeing the light flash against the dark night sky

Do you wonder about the people passing by?

Do they look at the lights in the window and see

The Temple, the brave Maccabees, and their victory?

Do they see the longing, the fighting, and the tears?

Do they see the yearning and the hope of the years?

You hope as you place the candles in the dark

That the lessons of Hanukkah soon find their mark;

That the message of candles shining in the night

Is of hope to the whole world to help set it right.

CHAPTER EIGHT

Peace

The Hanukkah story is a tale of the struggles, battles, and victory of the Maccabees over the Seleucids. But much more important, Hanukkah is about peace. It took many years, but finally the Maccabees regained the Temple, and the Jewish people were allowed to worship in peace once again. Tradition tells that the menorah had been taken away from the Temple, so the Jews took the enemy spears (the tools of war) and turned them into oil-holders so they could once again light the Temple menorah (the symbol of peace). It is true that the Jewish people had to fight for their religious freedom, but they were really fighting for peace. They did not want everyone else to believe as they did; they just wanted to have their own beliefs and to live in peace with their neighbors. Each Hanukkah, in homes and synagogues all over the world, the Jews light the candles of peace to remember the peace-seeking deeds of the Maccabees.

The concept of peace is one of the most important in the world. All people hope for a time when people of different races and religions can remember that we all share this Earth together and can live together in peace. The beautiful Hebrew word for peace is *shalom* (shah-LOHM).

The Jews have lived in many lands around the world for thousands of years. In each place, they have tried to live in peace with their neighbors. Sometimes it has been very difficult to maintain peace, but it is our responsibility to try. The prophets, wise teachers, taught that the Jewish people have a special job: to deliver the message of peace to the world.

The theme of peace is part of Hanukkah celebrations around the world, a time to make peace with others. In an offering of friendship and peace, gifts or services are given to family members, women, teachers, the caretaker of the synagogue, and the poor. Hanukkiyot made in Morocco sometimes include representations of two doves, the birds of peace, pointing the way to the

The Peace of Hanukkah

Peace in the country,
Peace up above;
A time of peace
Is a time of love.

Maccabees brave
Fought for our rights;
Now we honor them
For these eight nights.

The right to worship,
The right to pray,
Won in times ancient
And remembered today.

Blessings of love,
Blessings of peace;
May we live together
And may wars cease.

Peace in the country,
Peace up above;
A time of peace
Is a time of love.

77

"See the Conquering Hero Comes"

words by Thomas Morrell; from G. F. Handel's "Judas Maccabaeus"

In England in 1746, the famous composer George Frederick Handel composed a beautiful piece of music, an oratorio entitled <u>Judas Maccabaeus</u>, to honor the victory of Prince William, the Duke of Cumberland. ♪

See, the conqu'ring hero comes!
Sound the trumpets, beat the drums.
Sports prepare, the laurel bring,
Songs of triumph to him sing.
See the godlike youth advance!
Breathe the flutes and lead the dance.
Myrtle wreaths and roses twine,
To deck the hero's brow divine.

"Oseh Shalom"

עֹשֶׂה שָׁלוֹם בִּמְרוֹמָיו.
הוּא יַעֲשֶׂה שָׁלוֹם עָלֵינוּ
יַעַל־כָּל־יִשְׂרָאֵל. וְאִמְרוּ אָמֵן:

Oseh shalom bimromav.
Hu ya-aseh shalom
Aleynu v'al kol Yisrael.
V'im'ru ameyn.

May the One who makes peace in the heavens
Make peace for us and for all Israel. And say "Amen."

shammash candle. In Greece on the seventh night of Hanukkah, the girls try to make peace with friends or relatives whom they may have wronged.

The stories and activities in this section are about peace within ourselves, in our country, and in the world. What can you do this Hanukkah to help bring peace? Can you do something to help someone else? Make up with someone you have argued with recently? Plan a special peaceful family event? You could plan an evening of family games or story sharing, or create a meal with everyone working together, and invite friends to join you. Peace begins with each of us, one step at a time.

The Jews of Morocco fasted on the last day of Hanukkah. They would not talk all day, to make up for anything that they may have said that was not peaceful.

In 1790 the first United States president, George Washington, sent a letter to the Newport, Rhode Island, synagogue promising that people of all beliefs would be able to worship as they wished in peace.

In Amsterdam at the end of December 1943, Anne Frank, along with her family and several other people, was in hiding from the Nazis in the tiny attic of a building. The family celebrated Hanukkah by making little presents for each other and for the Christian couple who helped them. Anne wrote in her famous diary: "We haven't had such peace in the house for at least half a year."

During World War II, some of the Jewish people in the concentration camps wanted to be able to celebrate Hanukkah, a holiday celebrating peace. They saved bits of fat and butter to make candles or oil, made a candle holder out of an old potato, made wicks from threads they took from their clothes, and created Hanukkah menorahs. As each menorah was lit, the people prayed for peace to come soon.

The Hebrew word for peace is <u>shalom</u>. The Arab word for peace is <u>salaam</u>. It is almost the same word, and it means the same thing. When you light your hanukkiya, remember to say a prayer for peace in all the world.

Sweet Couscous

Couscous (KOOS-koos) is semolina, a ricelike grain that is served in many countries of the Sephardic world. The Jews of Spanish origin eat sweet couscous on the sixth night of Hanukkah to remind them of the sweet taste of peace. They were expelled from Spain in 1492, and some finally found peace in North Africa, where couscous is a traditional dish. The fruits and nuts used are reminders of the foods that the Maccabees ate while they were fighting for peace.

INGREDIENTS FOR COUSCOUS FOR 4 TO 6 PEOPLE:

⅓ *cup honey*

¼ *cup apricot preserves*

Juice of ½ lemon

1 teaspoon cinnamon

⅓ *teaspoon turmeric*

1 cup warm water

½ *cup chopped dried apricots*

⅓ *cup golden raisins*

⅓ *cup chopped prunes*

⅓ *cup almond pieces*

⅓ *cup cashew pieces*

enough uncooked couscous to make 4 cups of cooked couscous (cooking directions vary)

DIRECTIONS FOR MAKING COUSCOUS:

1. Mix the honey, preserves, lemon juice, cinnamon, and turmeric in a pot with the warm water. Heat the mixture on medium heat until the ingredients are mixed well but not boiling. Let the sauce cook for 10 minutes on low heat. Add the fruits and nuts, mix well, and let cook for another 5 to 7 minutes, until the fruits are soft.

2. While the sauce is cooking, prepare the couscous according to package directions.

3. Fluff the couscous with a fork and pour it into a large bowl. Make a hole in the middle of the couscous and pour the sauce onto the couscous.

Variations:

You can use any dried fruits and nuts that you like for the couscous. Other dried fruits include apples, pears, papaya, mango, and pineapple. Other nuts include walnuts, pecans, hazelnuts, and pine nuts.

Latkes Aren't Just for Hanukkah

A STORY OF MY FAMILY

It was one afternoon in the middle of the winter. I was about ten years old, and my mother and I were carrying on the tradition that she and her mother had shared when my mom was my age, many years before. It is a Hanukkah tradition in Jewish homes that has been followed for hundreds of years. It was the afternoon before the first night of Hanukkah, and we were peeling potatoes to make latkes.

"I love making latkes," I told my mother. "I wish we could have them all year long!" My mother started to laugh, and her dark eyes sparkled. "What's so funny?" I asked.

"Latkes aren't just for Hanukkah," she answered. "We could have them every day, if we wanted to. When I was growing up, we used to have them many times during the year."

"Wow! You were so lucky!"

"At the time we didn't think so; potatoes are cheap and filling. But that's not the only reason that we would have them. It was for the soldiers."

"Soldiers? What do soldiers have to do with latkes?"

"Do you mean that I have never told you about the soldiers and the latkes? Well, keep peeling those potatoes, and listen to how latkes helped to win World War II."

So I sat on the kitchen stool, peeling potatoes, then grating them into the big bowl, and listened to my mother as she wove a beautiful and delicious story of latkes. As she talked, the world of the early 1940s came alive again, and I could see my mother as a teenager and her mother (my Bubie) in the big, yellow kitchen of their cozy brick house. My mother, Dorothy, her sister, Lucille, and their friends Florrie, Evelyn, and Libbie had just returned from a dance, bringing with them eight soldiers dressed in their uniforms. The soldiers were stationed in Denver that winter.

"Hi, girls," said my Bubie. "Who did you bring home this time? Welcome to our house," she said to their guests. "You are lucky. One of your father's customers at the tailor shop just paid his bill with eggs from his farm! I've got ten pounds of potatoes and some extra matzoh meal, so I guess we can make potato latkes! What do you think?"

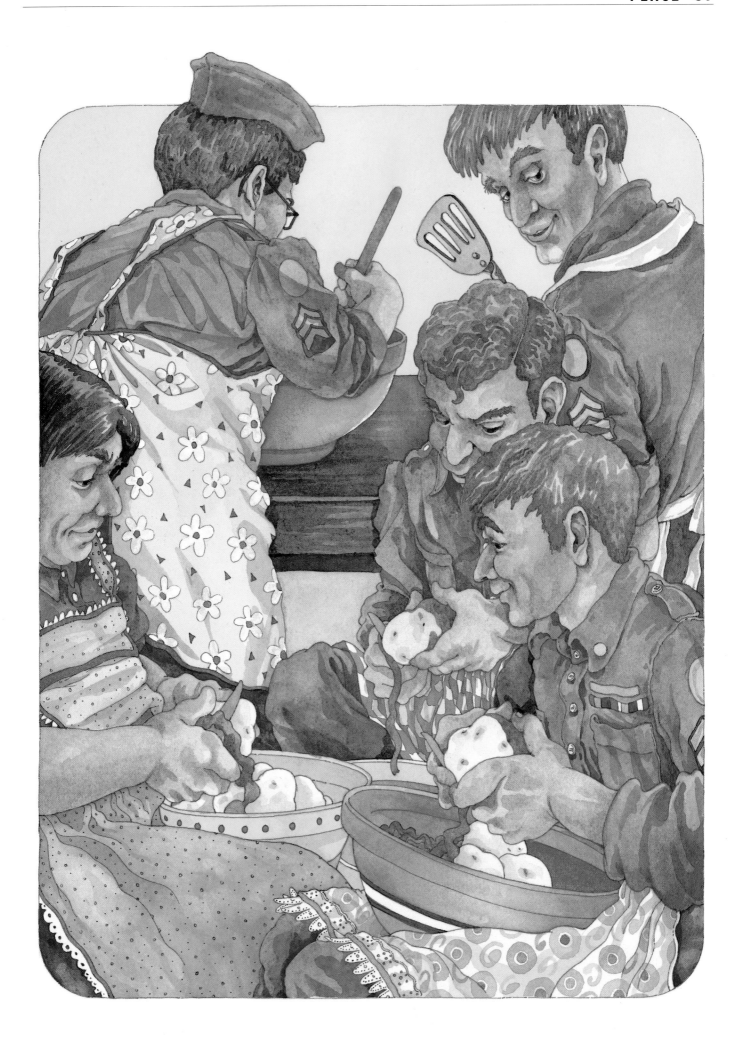

"Thanks, Mom," said Dorothy. "You're wonderful! We were just thinking of how delicious some warm latkes would be on a cold day like this. Now you can leave the kitchen, and we promise we'll clean up at the end. We'll even save some latkes for you and Daddy!"

"Thanks, Mrs. Olesh," called one of the soldiers named Bill. "How did you know what we wanted? Potato latkes are one homecooked Jewish food that we really miss." It was true. All of the soldiers wanted latkes. They loved them on Hanukkah, on other holidays, and on all days in between, too. Latkes reminded them of home, and of their Jewish connection.

Then the fun began. "Come on, boys!" said Lucille. "Before you can start cooking you need one of these beautiful, frilly, lacy aprons. You don't want to get your handsome uniforms all messed up, do you? Put them on!" So they did. The soldiers did all of the work while the girls just supervised and gave them lots of encouragement.

"Imagine this," my mother continued as I sat in the kitchen, still peeling potatoes. "There were all these soldiers in uniforms and lacy aprons, sitting in your Bubie's big kitchen, next to the big black stove, keeping warm. Each soldier was busy at his job. One was washing and peeling potatoes, one was grating potatoes, and one was grating onions. Others added matzoh meal, eggs, salt, and pepper. One would mix all the ingredients together. Finally, the soldiers stood over the hot stove frying the latkes in lots of oil. The room was filled with orders and requests, the sound of sizzling oil, and lots of laughter. The war seemed far, far away."

"These latkes look like they're worth all the work!" laughed one of the soldiers.

"Hey! You'd better keep a close eye on that back pan, or the latkes will all burn and then you'll have to start all over!" shouted Florrie, who was setting the table.

Soon the latkes were all made. Comments came from all over the kitchen.

"Yum! These taste best right from the pan."

"Stop stealing them or there'll be no more left at the table."

"Who's got the sour cream? Oh, wow! Will you look at that! Homemade applesauce! You girls are wonderful!"

"Yes, so wonderful that we got you boys to do all of the work. But we have to admit: the latkes are great."

"These are the best latkes we've ever tasted. They're even better than my mom's, but promise that you'll never tell her," said one of the soldiers. My Bubie, who had poked her head into the dining room to see what all the commotion was about, just smiled.

"Have another latke. It couldn't hurt you. Eat! We'll say that you ate anyway!" she told them. And then she disappeared into the kitchen to clean up while the boys and girls ate and laughed and told each other stories, and almost forgot about the war.

"What a wonderful story!" I told my mother. You were lucky to have the soldiers to peel and grate the potatoes for you. It's hard work. Tell me more of the story, so I'll forget that my hands and arms are getting so tired." So my mother continued.

"The soldiers came at all times of the year and always wanted the famous potato latkes, and they also came at Hanukkah to help light the candles and say the blessings and, of course, to gobble latkes. Sometimes the soldiers brought us small gifts, but their biggest gift was sharing the miracles of Hanukkah with us. Sometimes, it seemed a miracle that a small bag of potatoes could feed all of those big soldiers."

And that is the story that my mother told me while we were sitting in our cozy kitchen in the middle of the winter, waiting for the sun to go down, for the start of another Hanukkah. And that year, the latkes tasted especially warm and good and delicious. My mom tells me that Bubie felt that it was her role in the war to help make the soldiers feel a little better, a little less lonely and afraid, and a little more Jewish, by having them help make latkes.

Many of the soldiers wrote to Mom and her friends, and they answered. And some-times, the mother of one of the soldiers would write to my mom's family to say thank you for the gift of latkes, a gift of remembrance. It may just be that by eating the latkes all year-round, the miracles of Hanukkah were remembered, which may, in some small way, have helped to bring peace.

Peace Mats

During the time that the Maccabees fought to regain the Temple, their real goal was peace. The Jewish people wanted peace so that they could practice their religion as they wished. We all hope for peace in our homes, in our synagogues, with our neighbors, and in the world. Here is a craft to celebrate peace. You can make a peace mat to use under your hanukkiya. The peace mat serves two purposes: it will help keep the candle wax from dripping on furniture and it adds beauty to the hanukkiya, the symbol of peace.

The peace mats can also be used at your table. You can use a peace mat as a centerpiece for your Hanukkah meal with family and friends.

MATERIALS:

scraps of colored and patterned paper, fabrics, ribbons, lace, photographs

pictures cut from magazines or last year's greeting cards

foil letters

markers, crayons, paints

glitter, sequins, confetti, foil stars

2 8½ × 11-inch sheets of paper

roll of clear plastic contact paper

scissors

glue

INSTRUCTIONS:

1. Gather together things to create a collage, an arrangement of different materials placed together in an interesting design. Use images that show peace in your family, peace in your community, and peace in your world. Some good ideas might include: the Earth, family photographs, doves, rainbows, people holding hands, nature scenes, and names of people close to you.

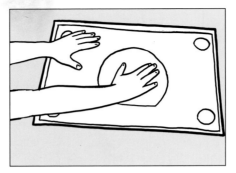

2. Tape two 8½ × 11-inch pieces of colored paper together along the long edge on both sides to form an 11 × 17-inch rectangle. Lay the rectangle flat on a table, and arrange the images you've collected in a pleasing pattern. You can surround the world with hands touching, stars, and Jewish stars, and make glitter clouds. You can use lace or ribbon to frame photographs. Use foil letters to add a message, such as "shalom" or "peace." You can write the names of people close to you in marker or crayon.

3. Once you have decided on your arrangement, glue or stick each piece to the colored paper.

4. Cut two pieces of contact paper, 12 × 18 inches each.

5. Remove the backing from one piece of the contact paper and set it flat on the table with the sticky side up.

6. Carefully pick up the collage paper and center it on the 12 × 18-inch sheet of contact paper. Press it down flat.

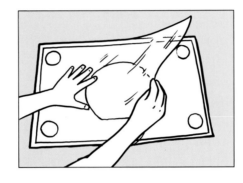

7. After everything is in place, have an adult help you carefully remove the backing from the second sheet of contact paper. Starting from one edge of the mat, slowly lay it over the top, rubbing it flat as you go. Press out any air bubbles or creases as you go.

8. If the two pieces of contact paper do not meet exactly, trim the edges with scissors or on a cutting board.

What the Maccabees Fought For

What the Maccabees fought for
those many years ago
was not just for a piece of land
or to defeat the foe.

It wasn't the glory of their people
so they could prove their might;
to show the world what they could do,
to set the whole world right.

It wasn't to make the world love them
or even to act like them, too;
or to have the world think like them
and pray the same as they do.

No.
What the Maccabees fought for
What the small army cried for
what many brave soldiers died for
was
Peace.

Peace so they could worship in the Temple,
Peace so they would be able to pray,
Peace so they could live with their neighbors,
Peace to help them show the way.

Glossary

Here is a list of words used in this book that may not be familiar to you.

ANTIOCHUS IV (an-TIE-oh-kus): the king of the Seleucids, the enemy of the Jews at the time of the battle with the Maccabees

ARK: where the Torah scrolls (the five books of Moses) are kept in a synagogue

ASHKENAZIC (ahsh-ken-AHZ-ik): pertaining to the Jewish people from Central and Eastern European countries, or to their descendants

BAAL SHEM TOV (BAL SHEM TOVE): Hebrew words meaning "Master of the Good Name"; the name of Israel ben Eliezer, the Ukranian/Polish founder of the Hasidic movement in Judaism in the eighteenth century

BIMAH (BEE-mah): the platform, usually raised, from which the service in a synagogue is conducted

BOUREK (BOO-rek): a Turkish cheese pie in a flaky pastry crust

BUBBEH (BUH-beh): a Yiddish word for grandmother

COUSCOUS (KOOS-koos): a Middle Eastern semolina grain in small round shape, used like rice

DREIDEL (DRAY-duhl): the four-sided top for Hanukkah. It has Hebrew letters on each side that stand for the phrase "a great miracle happened there."

GABBAI (GA-by): the person who stands next to the person who is reading from the Torah during services and makes sure that all the words are pronounced correctly

GELT: a Yiddish word for money, often used for coins given to children on Hanukkah

GONDOLA (Italian; GON-doh-lah): a long, narrow, flat-bottomed boat rowed by one person standing in the back

HAMSA (HAHM-sah): an ornamental symbol made in the shape of a hand, meant to protect and guard the owner from harm

HANUKKIYA/plural **HANUKKIYOT** (hah-noo-kee-YAH/OTE): modern Hebrew name for the Hanukkah menorah, with eight lights and one higher than the rest

HASMONEANS (haz-muh-nee-uhns) a dynasty of Jewish rulers over Judea descended from the Maccabees

HASIDIC (hah-SID-ik): of or about the Orthodox sect of Jews who follow the principles of the Baal Shem Tov of the eighteenth century of religious strictness, prayer, and joy

HATIKVAH (hah-teek-VAH): the Hebrew word for "hope"; the Israeli national anthem written as a poem in 1878 by Naphtali Herz Imber (nahf-TAH-lee herts imbr) and set to music by Samuel Cohen

HILLEL (HIL-el): a wise teacher of first century BCE Babylon and Israel known for his knowledge and his judgment. He had a series of debates with Shammai about interpretations of the law

HOLOFERNES (ho-loh-FER-nees): a general who was killed by the Jewish woman Judith

JUDAH MACCABEE (JOO-dah): the leader of the Maccabees, called "The Hammer"

JUDEA (ju-DEE-a): the ancient name for what is now Israel

JUDITH: a brave Jewish woman who saved the Jews

KIBBEH (KIB-ee): a Middle Eastern food made of ground lamb and pine nuts stuffed inside meatballs

LATKES (LAHT-kuhs): potato pancakes fried in oil, the most popular traditional food for Hanukkah

LOUKOUMADES (Greek; loo-koo-MAH-dehs): small round fried dough balls covered with honey and nuts

MACCABEE (MAK-ah-bee): derived from a Hebrew word for "hammer"; the name given to Judah and the others fighting for freedom from the Seleucids

MATTATHIUS (mat-ah-THIGH-us): the first leader of the Jewish people against the Seleucids, and the father of Judah and his brothers

MENORAH (men-OR-uh): the seven-branched candleholder that was originally used in the Temple in ancient times. It is also the name for the eight-branched lamp with one light higher, which is used on Hanukkah

MIRANDA DE HANUKKAH (mee-RAN-dah deh HA-noo-kah): a Hanukkah celebration of the Sephardic Jews. Children gather foods from neighbors, bring them to the synagogue, and then prepare feasts for orphans, widows, and the poor.

MODI'IN (moh-dee-EEN): the town in Judea where the Hanukkah story takes place

NER TAMID (nehr tah-MEED): the eternal light that always glows in a synagogue, usually placed above the ark

NES GADOL HAYA SHAM (nes ga-DOLE HAH-yah SHAHM): Hebrew words meaning "a great miracle happened there." The first letter of each of these words appears on the sides of a dreidel. The dreidels in Israel have a different last letter (pey) and different last word (po), meaning "here," because the miracle happened in Israel.

NEYYAPAM (nay-ah-PAHM): a southern Indian fried dough dessert made with fermented fruits

PASSOVER or **PESACH** (PEH-sahkh): the spring Jewish holiday celebrating the exodus from Egypt in ancient times

PURIM (poo-REEM): the spring holiday celebrating Queen Esther saving the Jews of Shushan

SELEUCIDS (si-LOO-sids): rulers of the Syrian Empire and enemies of the Maccabee soldiers and the Jews

SEPHARDIC (seh-FAR-dik): pertaining to the Jewish people from Spain or Portugal and their descendants living in many countries

SHALOM (shah-LOME): a Hebrew word for peace, hello, and good-bye. The word in Arabic is very similar: salaam (sa-LAHM)

SHAMMAI (SHAH-my): a wise teacher who lived in the first century BCE and who was a colleague of Hillel. Shammai and Hillel often debated interpretations of the law

SHAMMES (Yiddish; SHAH-mes;) or **SHAMMASH** (Hebrew; shah-MAHSH;): the one candle that stands taller or off to the side from the rest of the candles in the Hanukkah lamp; also, the caretaker of the synagogue

TIROPITA (tir-OH-pee-tah): a Greek cheese pie in a flaky filo (pastry leaf) dough

ɔliography

Burns, Marilyn. *The Hanukkah Book*. New York: Four Winds Press, 1981.

Chaiken, Miriam. *Light Another Candle: The Story and Meaning of Hanukkah.* New York: Clarion Books, 1981.

Drucker, Malka. *Hanukkah: Eight Nights, Eight Lights*. New York: Holiday House, 1980.

Frishman, Elyse D. *Hanerot Halalu. These Lights are Holy: A Home Celebration of Hanukkah*. New York: The Central Conference of American Rabbis, 1989.

Goodman, Phillip. *The Hanukkah Anthology*. Philadelphia: The Jewish Publication Society of America, 1976.

Groner, Judye, and Madeline Wikler. *All About Hanukkah*. Rockville, Md.: Kar-Ben Copies Inc., 1988.

Rockland, Mae Schafter. *The Hanukkah Book*. New York: Schocken Books, 1975.

Rosenblum, William F. and Robert J. *Eight Lights: The Story of Hanukkah*. New York: Doubleday, 1967.

Rush, Barbara, and Eliezer Marcus. *Seventy and One Tales for the Jewish Year: Folktales for the Festivals*. New York: AZYF, 1980.

Scherman, Rabbi Nosson, and Rabbi Meir Zlotowitz, eds. *Chanukah: Its History, Observance and Significance.* New York: Mesorah Publications Ltd. (Art Scroll), 1981.

Schram, Peninnah, and Steven M. Rossman. *Eight Tales for Eight Nights*. New York: Jason Aronson Inc., 1990.

Solis-Cohen, Emily. *Hanukkah: The Feast of Lights.* Philadelphia: The Jewish Publication Society of America, 1937.

Sussman, Susan. *Hanukkah: Eight Nights Around the World*. Morton Grove, Ill.: Albert Whitman & Co., 1988.

Wolfson, Ron. *The Art of Jewish Living: Hanukkah*. New York: Federation of Jewish Men's Clubs and the University of Judaism, 1990.

Index